43- 16708

To Jack
from Vinier
1944 -

D1217688

HAPPY STORIES
Just To Laugh At

Books by
STEPHEN LEACOCK

❖❖❖❖❖❖

LITERARY LAPSES

NONSENSE NOVELS

SUNSHINE SKETCHES

THE UNSOLVED RIDDLE OF SOCIAL JUSTICE

AFTERNOONS IN UTOPIA

HELLEMENTS OF HICKONOMICS

MODEL MEMOIRS

TOO MUCH COLLEGE

THE BRITISH EMPIRE

MY REMARKABLE UNCLE

LAUGH WITH LEACOCK

STEPHEN LEACOCK'S LAUGH PARADE

HOW TO WRITE

OUR HERITAGE OF LIBERTY

HAPPY STORIES

JUST TO LAUGH AT

By
STEPHEN LEACOCK

NEW YORK
DODD, MEAD AND COMPANY
1943

PRINTED IN THE UNITED STATES OF AMERICA
BY THE CORNWALL PRESS, CORNWALL, N. Y.

PREFACE

ALL THE STORIES in this book have, or are meant to have, one element in common. They are not true to life. The people in them laugh too much; they cry too easily; they lie too hard. The light is all false, it's too bright, and the manners and customs are all wrong. The times and places are confused.

There is no need, therefore, to give the usual assurance that none of the characters in the book are real persons. Of course not; this is not real life. It is better.

STEPHEN LEACOCK

CONTENTS

CONTENTS

HAPPY STORIES
Just To Laugh At

I

MR. McCOY SAILS FOR FIJI

SOMETIMES you get a lesson in life. Something occurs to
show you that your career, after all, no matter how successful, hasn't amounted to so much—is, in fact, a pretty selfish
business. How much did you ever do for anybody beside
yourself?

You get this feeling when brought into contact with men
you knew early in life, and lost from sight—when you find
such men with success twice as big as your own, and a life
behind them filled with all sorts of things done for other
people . . . and with that, a complete modesty about it all,
almost an unconsciousness of what they have done.

I felt all that when I met—or rather re-met after years and
years—my friend McIvor McCoy. It was out on the big grass
lawn of the Empress Hotel—you know it, of course—in Victoria B.C., on such a lovely morning—but it's always a lovely
morning there—all flowers and springtime and the ruffled
Pacific Ocean reaching away to eternity.

There stood McCoy, as easy and debonair as ever, with his
old-time way of seeming balanced on his toes, swaying faintly
in the light breeze, such a cheery, affable, nut-brown elderly
man—old? Well, yes, I suppose, but with something of timeless youth still about him. Neatly but loosely dressed he was,
in a suit of careless but expensive grey with little touches of
an older fashion: a flower in his buttonhole, a signet ring,

1

seals on his watch chain and the grey Homburg hat of years ago . . .

"Well, well," he said, "well, well!"—and it sounded the pleasantest thing in the world to say—"Come and sit on this bench and let's talk—"

"What a charming place," he began, "and the ocean, how wonderful! I've just been congratulating the hotel manager"—he spoke with a certain dignity as of one whose congratulation meant something—"been congratulating the manager on the ocean."

Now look at that. I would never have thought of congratulating the manager on the Pacific Ocean . . . I wouldn't have realized that he put it there. Yet in a sense he did; he might have put the hotel a hundred miles inland in the bush . . .

It began to bring back McCoy to me. He was like that; always congratulating people on things—with the quiet dignity of a Scottish laird recognizing merit . . .

"And such a charming hotel," he continued. "These wonderful corridors; I had quite a romp with some of the children in them this morning . . . I gave them all some candy."

Now, there again. "Did you know them?" I asked. "No, no—just children in the hotel. There are always children in a hotel. That's why I carry candy."

Now, could I do that? Well, I guess not. How do you romp with children? What do you say first? It beat me.

"Let's move to that other bench," said Mr. McCoy, rising, "the one over there."

"Why do we do that?" I asked; I saw no particular need to move.

"I'm interested in benches just now," said Mr. McCoy . . .
"I've invented a folding bench, a legless bench that folds up
into a single piece . . . a total weight of five pounds . . . the
only question is a matter of strain . . . now, sit at the very
end . . ."

Then I remembered, of course, that McCoy, even from our
college days, was an inventor. He took honour physics and
mechanics and was always tinkering with inventions—queer
inventions like this legless bench—a fireless cooker, and an
iceless refrigerator, and a soundless telephone—things no one
else would think of. I remember, even as a student he got five
hundred dollars for an automatic electric street car bell, to
ring immediately after they ran over anybody. There was
quite a lot of talk about it but afterwards it was criticized—I
forget why.

"And what a charming old town—" continued McCoy . .
"I went yesterday up that old street on the right behind us"
—he waved his hand over his shoulder—"part of the original
town, quite abandoned now—but such very interesting old
people in the shops, many from Scotland, still wistful for the
Hebrides. I gave them," he said, "each an American dollar—
to one poor old fellow, from Huish itself, the most wistful,
I gave five."

There it was again. I'd been up that street—to buy a note-
book. I didn't know they were wistful. I didn't know they
were worrying about the Hebrides. They seemed just old
people in old shops. If I'd known about the Hebrides I'd
have given them—well, ten cents anyway . . .

Incidentally I realized that Mr. McCoy must be well off
. . . Presently, when he began to tell me of all his inventions
and of the people he'd met—the governments and ministers—

I realized that of course he must be, simply rolling in it. Imagine sitting with the Pope discussing the heating of the Vatican with explosive magnesium! I don't mean that he paraded these things; that was his least idea. They just came out in conversation. As I say, imagine sitting down with the Hospodar of Transylvania—I'll swear I never knew who he was—to discuss blowing up the Iron Gates of the Danube to supply electricity to the Balkans.

But that was the way it was with Mr. McCoy. You see I call him *Mr.* McCoy, in writing, because he seemed so dignified. Of course I called him McIvor when we spoke, though in a way he seemed a new and strange person.

I was certainly impressed, even at the very start, when I asked him where he was bound for and he answered cheerily and casually, "Fiji, very possibly, but I'm not quite decided."

Then I realized that there was a big steamer lying at the dock down below—it's only a couple of hundred yards—with rags of smoke coming out of the funnels, dull raucous blowings from time to time, and that moving of cabs, trucks and little figures on the dock that indicates a departing liner.

"Fiji," he said, "but I'm not certain . . ."

"Don't you have to have a passport?"

He laughed easily.

"I carry plenty of them," he said. "They let me have all I want . . ."

Here was another touch of unconscious importance, but no affectation about it.

But it was his mention of the Hebrides that had brought him back most clearly to my mind, as I recalled him from our college days.

Let me explain:

We were classmates for years. My old friend's name is not really McCoy, but McIvor McCoy, written not with a little c but with an apostrophe and indeed properly spelt Mc-Quohy. The McCoys came originally from Huish—or Huosh —in the Inner Hebrides, that is, after they moved in from the Outer Hebrides. The family escutcheon is two thistles and a dagger with the motto *Creagh-na-Skaw*. The present head of the clan is Lord Coy who is, of course, the McCoy, though oddly enough he is not the McIvor. His eldest son is. Their present seat is McCoy Castle which hangs on the edge of a skaw in the Inverness country. Tourists pay a shilling to go through the grounds and walk out on the stone platform that overlooks the steep drop of the skaw. Some pay more. One or two, it is said, who didn't pay, have fallen over. The family motto *Creagh-na-Skaw* is cut in the stone. It means Watch-Your-Step. But it's Gaelic. They do say that in the old Highland days—but of course that's just talk.

It goes without saying that the McCoys were out in the "Forty Five," every man of them, out and back. My friend is very proud of a dirk of the Young Pretender that they have at McCoy Castle; they have his dirk, and his gold watch and chain, and his gold pencil, and his cuff-links. The Young Pretender, it seems, while in hiding in Scotland, spent a night at McCoy Castle.

You will wonder how I could remember all these details. But they all came back to me in a flood of memory when I met McCoy . . . .This used to be his talk at college—so much so, that the other students used to like to take a rise out of him, ask him if he'd heard lately from Lord Coy, and how the Duke of Inverness was keeping, and rag him about Mc-Coy Castle.

McIvor never saw it. He had too much Highland dignity . . .

So, naturally, I found myself beginning to laugh at the recollection of it all, and saying,

"Have you ever seen your kinsman, Lord Coy, in your travels?"

"Oh, yes," he answered. "I've been at McCoy Castle several times. The first time I sent Lord Coy a salmon rod with a reel I'd invented which he was good enough to accept . . . He invited me to Coy Castle—that is, I came with the rod and he invited me in . . . I came back later and brought him an exact replica of the Pretender's gold watch, which I asked him to accept."

"Did he?" I asked.

"He did," said Mr. McCoy, with dignity, "as head of the clan. He was delighted with the workmanship. He said that the only way to distinguish the original from the replica was that one had a chain and the other had not . . . I sent him a chain from London—without, of course, any forewarning, so as to forestall all refusal."

"Did it forestall it?"

"It did," said Mr. McCoy . . . "We'll shift, if you don't mind, to that further bench . . ."

Then he went on talking of his own prompting, as it seemed.

. . . "Once again I went to Coy Castle, bringing with me a valiseful of high explosive, of very high explosive; and boring tools."

"Good Lord!" I exclaimed. "What for?"

"I showed Lord Coy a plan for damming the river below the skaw, blowing a tunnel under his castle and driving fifty thousand hydro-electric volts right through it . . ."

"What did he say?" I asked.

"His Lordship," said Mr. McCoy, choosing his words with care, "was tremendously impressed. He at once took me out on the stone parapet that overhangs the ravine. I showed him the method of a safety clutch that could be installed to prevent accident. We came in again . . . He immediately, that very night, had a man take me to Edinburgh to look up the records . . . The man, by mistake, took me clear to London . . ."

"And what came of it?" I asked.

"Nothing," said Mr. McCoy, "nothing. That often happens." A momentary shadow passed over his face.

I realized that, after all, the life of an inventor must have its trials. Think of that dull Scottish nobleman. Utterly unaware of progress. McCoy offers to blow up his castle. Does he see it? No. I more than suspected—I am inclined to see through things of this sort pretty easily—that it was not by mistake that the man took Mr. McCoy all the way to London.

"That was too bad," I said.

"No, no, oh, no," said Mr. McCoy, recovering himself in that quick happy way he had . . . "It was of no consequence. In any case I was just due to start for Holland . . ."

"Holland?" I said.

"The Zuyder Zee," he answered. "You may have read of the recovery of the flooded land of Holland where the Zuyder Zee broke in, hundreds of years ago."

"Oh, yes," I said.

"It was recovered," he said, "in polders by the sinking of caissons banded together with a welded network."

Technical terms flowed easily from Mr. McCoy . . . What

a wonderful thing it must be, to be an engineer! What a lot they know.

"That was my work," Mr. McCoy continued, "all mine. I brought the plans over in a sealed tube . . . It was stolen . . . or rather not *stolen* . . . taken at the Customs and kept by the Government."

"What could you do?" I asked.

"I could get no redress . . . reasons of state . . . I saw Mynheer Van Ploop, the Minister President; he said it had to be . . . He was most affable but could do nothing . . . I asked if I might have an audience with the Queen . . . Impossible . . . I thought perhaps a little diplomacy . . . I asked leave to present Her Majesty with a beaten silver soup tureen, a large one . . ."

"Would she take it?"

"Not in person. Mr. Van Ploop presented it . . . She was most gracious; she has, you know, that plain almost rough way of all the family of Orange—'Vooksillig,' they call it in Dutch. We have no English for it. She said, 'Where's the spoon?' So of course I bought Mr. Van Ploop a large spoon . . ."

"Did he give it to her?"

"Oh, yes, he told me so himself. In fact, he was laughing about having paid the express on it out of his own pocket— till I stopped him . . . He was really most considerate . . . Had me taken across the frontier to avoid all danger."

"Good heavens!" I said. I began to see that life among the courts and chanceries of Europe is not easy.

To think how little they appreciate science! How little they care for progress. A man like McCoy having to sneak across their frontiers.

"You seem to have been treated pretty badly over there," I said.

"Oh, no," he answered, "not at all—or perhaps only once."

"Was that when you were called in to heat the Vatican?"

"Oh, no," protested Mr. McCoy, "His Holiness was most delightful . . . I was called in—I must be fair—not really *called* in—I *got* in, on a *laisser entrer* from the American Secretary . . . His Holiness was delightful . . . I explained to him my proposal for heating the Vatican by explosions of magnesium—in Latin, of course—I spoke in Latin entirely . . . The dear old man sat and nodded his head so gently, merely saying *hic . . . hoc.* But Cardinal Rampolla felt it was too much for him . . . He took me by the arm and simply insisted—in English, excellent English—on my going out . . . Oh, no, they were all delightful at the Vatican. In fact I was escorted under a papal guard to the Serbian frontier . . ."

"But that magnesium stuff—that sounds very wonderful. Doesn't the Pope understand Latin?"

"The word *explosio,*" said Mr. McCoy, "it may have mislead him. They so often have bombs carried in . . . But of course the thing is wonderful."

He was off again in his technical terms, more than I could follow, yet I am certain marvellously exact. That, it seems, is the idea about Fiji. Did you know—I didn't—that Fiji has the greatest natural magnesium springs in the world? And that these, if they can be turned to run over uranium ore, will solve the problem of the liberation of atomic energy for industrial power . . . Mr. McCoy intends to show the British High Commissioner at Fiji that with one teaspoonful of radiumized magnesium he can blow up Government House . . .

To think that Mr. McCoy has carried secrets like that all round Europe without recognition . . . And that reminded me . . .

"Where did you say, McIvor, you were actually mistreated —what was that?"

"Let us move," he said, "to the seat behind that trellis." He seemed for some reason to look over his shoulder as he said it . . . "That was in Belgrade." He paused, with the shadow on his face.

"What happened?"

"I was kidnapped." He paused again and then went on. "My plan had been to blow in the Iron Gates (the great rocks) of the Danube, thus creating unlimited power . . . I had made certain experiments with high explosive near the Gates themselves in the evenings . . . but the peasants are suspicious . . . I had even tried to interest those in control of the upper waters—the Ban of Dalmatia—I gave him a Smith & Wesson revolver, and the Hospodar of Transylvania —I gave him—let me see, yes—a five-bladed jacknife . . ."

"Well, what happened?"

"Finally I went to see Mr. Veryitch, the Prime Minister . . . I must admit his manner was charming; he gave me a cigarette."

"Good for him; and I bet you gave him a silver samovar, eh?"

"Indeed, no," said Mr. McCoy. "You little know the Serbs if you think that. They're a very proud people, especially men like Mr. Veryitch whose family have been Royal Cuspidors for a thousand years. You can't give watches and jewels and presents to them. I gave Mr. Veryitch five hundred dollars in American bills. It was all he would take. In fact it was all I had."

"Well—"

"Next morning I was kidnapped—kidnapped while I was feeding the swans in the public park—a new idea I'd worked out of feeding swans with a dust of compressed oxygen . . ."

Mr. McCoy paused. The recollection seemed painful . . . He got up and walked to the end of the trellis and looked around the corner of the leaves. Then he sat down again. I didn't like to question him. It seemed amazing that Europe, including people like the Serbs that we think the world of, should have been so blind.

It was some little time before Mr. McCoy spoke again. The shadow had fallen again upon his face—a sort of queer perplexity . . . such as one sees sometimes on the face of a puzzled child . . . indeed it made him look quite young again.

"It was six months before I could get out of Serbia . . . Mr. Veryitch must have heard of it . . . at any rate he sent me under escort, for security's sake, not only through Serbia but right across to a channel port . . . I thought it wise to travel under assumed names . . . in fact, I assumed several . . . the escort acquiesced in it entirely . . . I've since found it very useful . . ."

Mr. McCoy seemed trailing off into memories and lapses of silence. Then he began again with something of his own animation.

"In London, the Home Secretary was most concerned, most helpful. He thought that the only way to avoid a European complication would be to secrete me for some time in the country . . . I gave him a cigar. With him, I remember, that morning was Sir John Seeley—later, you know, Lord Mottistone. I gave him a pocketbook with a map of Hampshire—he comes from there, you know—he was delighted with

it. He said he would never have known it was Hampshire.
Perhaps it wasn't. I got it in Serbia."

Mr. McCoy went and looked round the trellis again. Perhaps it was the steamer. At any rate a long sonorous whistle
was blowing . . .

"One moment," said Mr. McCoy, and with that he slipped
sideways along the trellis and into the hotel somehow by the
back . . . At any rate he disappeared . . . I waited . . .
The steamer whistle was blowing again.

I came round back on to the lawn . . . As I did so, I saw
two men hurrying across the grass towards me. I didn't like
the look of either of them. I was quick enough to grasp at
once what it might mean; if this was another attempt to kid-
nap Mr. McCoy, I wanted nothing to do with it.

At any rate the men looked exactly it. One of them was in
the dress of an hotel attendant, a disguise, of course, only too
easy to assume and seen through at once. The other wore a
sort of pretence of a police inspector's uniform, a very good
imitation but transparent enough also as he had no number
on his neck and no badge—yet I will admit that when he
reached me and spoke, his voice was certainly well schooled
for the part.

"You were with a gentleman in grey, sir?" he asked.

I hesitated what to do; but supposed that all I had to do
was to answer truthfully but give no extra information, so I
said yes.

"Can you tell me where he is now?"

"No," I said, "I can't."

Yet I thought at that moment I could see an open carriage
driving from the hotel to the dock, and in it, I was almost
certain, was Mr. McCoy . . .

"Did he tell you where he was going?" persisted the man,

and he added, "I may tell you that it's only his friends who are looking for him."

That was a little too thin.

"No," I said, "not in definite terms. We were talking of other things."

"Are you aware," the man went on, "that you were talking with the Hospodar of Transylvania travelling incognito as the Ban of Dalmatia?"

He spoke with a sort of sneer that made me angry.

"No," I said, "and if you want to know it, the gentleman is nothing of that sort at all, but an old college friend of mine that I've known for thirty years. He has no connection with Europe and is most likely going to Fiji."

"Fiji!" they both exclaimed, "Fiji! We should have thought of it." And off they went down the slope of the grass, running for the dock. I could see the gangway of the steamer being hauled in. Mr. McCoy I couldn't see.

They failed to make it. I saw the steamer pull slowly away from the dock. I expected to see it stopped. If the man were *really* an inspector surely he could have had it stopped . . . But no . . . Away, away it went . . . till it was a cloud of smoke away out on the horizon.

When I went in to lunch I looked over the steamer passenger list as given in the morning paper. Mr. McCoy's name was not there. But it occurred to me that that didn't mean anything. If Mr. McCoy only got on board at the last minute his name wouldn't be on the list. But, oddly enough, the other fellow's name was—there it was large as life—the Hereditary Ban of Dalmatia, passenger for Fiji.

It set me thinking—almost.

II

PAWN TO KING'S FOUR

(There is no readier escape from the ills of life than in a game of chess.—Francis Bacon, and Eggs.)

"PAWN to King's Four," I said as I sat down to the chess table.

"Pawn to King's Four, eh?" said Letherby, squaring himself comfortably to the old oak table, his elbows on its wide margin, his attitude that of the veteran player. "Pawn to King's Four," he repeated. "Aha, let's see!"

It's the first and oldest move in chess, but from the way Letherby said it you'd think it was as new as yesterday . . . Chess players are like that . . . "Pawn to King's Four," he repeated. "You don't mind if I take a bit of a think over it?"

"No, no," I said, "not at all. Play as slowly as you like. I want to get a good look round this wonderful room."

It was the first time I had ever been in the Long Room of the Chess Club—and I sat entranced with the charm and silence of the long wainscotted room—its soft light, the blue tobacco smoke rising to the ceiling—the open grate fires burning—the spaced-out tables, the players with bent heads, unheeding our entry and our presence . . . all silent except here and there a little murmur of conversation, that rose only to hush again.

"Pawn to King's Four"—repeated Letherby—"let me see!"

14

It was, I say, my first visit to the Chess Club; indeed I had never known where it was except that it was somewhere down town, right in the heart of the city, among the big buildings. Nor did I know Letherby himself very well, though I had always understood he was a chess player. He looked like one. He had the long, still face, the unmoving eyes, the leathery, indoor complexion that marks the habitual chess player anywhere.

So, quite naturally, when Letherby heard that I played chess he invited me to come round some night to the Chess Club . . . "I didn't know you played," he said. "You don't look like a chess player—I beg your pardon, I didn't mean to be rude."

So there we were at the table. The Chess Club, as I found, was right down town, right beside the New Commercial Hotel; in fact, we met by agreement in the rotunda of the hotel . . . a strange contrast—the noise, the lights, the racket of the big rotunda, the crowding people, the call of the bellboys—and this unknown haven of peace and silence, somewhere just close above and beside it.

I have little sense of location and direction so I can't say just how you get to the Club—up a few floors in the elevator and along a corridor (I think you must pass out of the building here) and then up a queer little flight of stairs, up another little stairway and with that all at once you come through a little door, a sort of end-corner door in the room and there you are in the Long Room . . .

"Pawn to King's Four," said Letherby, decided at last, moving the piece forward . . . "I thought for a minute of opening on the Queen's side, but I guess not."

All chess players think of opening on the Queen's side but never do. Life ends too soon.

"Knight to Bishop's Three," I said.

"Knight to Bishop's Three, aha!" exclaimed Letherby, "oho!" and went into a profound study . . . It's the second oldest move in chess; it was old three thousand years ago in Persepolis . . . but to the real chess player it still has all the wings of the morning.

So I could look round again, still fascinated with the room.

"It's a beautiful room, Letherby," I said.

"It is," he answered, his eyes on the board, "yes . . . yes . . . It's really part of the old Roslyn House that they knocked down to make the New Commercial . . . It was made of a corridor and a string of bedrooms turned into one big room. That's where it got the old wainscotting and those old-fashioned grate fires."

I had noticed them, of course, at once—the old-fashioned grates, built flat into the wall, the coal bulging and glowing behind bars, with black marble at the side and black marble for the mantel above . . . There were three of them, one at the side, just near us, one down the room and one across the end . . . But from none of them came noise or crackle —just a steady warm glow. Beside the old-fashioned grate stood the long tongs, and the old-fashioned poker with the heavy square head that went with it.

"Pawn to Queen's Third," said Letherby.

Nor in all the room was there a single touch of equipment that was less than of fifty years ago, a memory of a half century . . . Even the swinging doors, panelled with Russian leather, the main entrance on the right hand at the furthest end, swung soundlessly, on their hinges as each noiseless member entered with a murmured greeting.

"Your move," said Letherby. "Bishop to Bishop's Four? Right." . . . Most attractive of all, perhaps, was a little railed-in place at the side near the fire place, all done in old oak . . . something between a bar and a confessional, with coffee over low blue flames, and immaculate glasses on shelves . . . lemons in a bag . . . Round it moved a waiter, in a dinner jacket, the quietest, most unobstrusive waiter one ever saw . . . coffee to this table . . . cigars to that . . . silent work with lemons behind the rails . . . a waiter who seemed to know what the members wanted without their asking . . . This must have been so, for he came over to our table presently and set down long glasses of Madeira—so old, so brown, so aromatic that there seemed to go up from it with the smoke clouds, a vision of the sunny vineyards beside Funchal . . . Such at least were the fancies that my mind began to weave around this enchanted place . . . And the waiter, too, I felt there must be some strange romance about him; no one could have a face so mild, yet with the stamp of tragedy upon it . . .

I must say—in fact, I said to Letherby—I felt I'd like to join the club, if I could. He said, oh, yes, they took in new members. One came in only three years ago.

"Queen's Knight to Bishop's Third," said Letherby with a deep sigh. I knew he had been thinking of something that he daren't risk. All chess is one long regret.

We played on like that for—it must have been half an hour —anyway we played four moves each. To me, of course, the peace and quiet of the room was treat enough . . . but to Letherby, as I could see, the thing was not a sensation of peace but a growing excitement, nothing still or quiet about it; a rush, struggle—he knew that I meant to strike in on the King's side. Fool! he was thinking, that he hadn't advanced the Queen's Pawn another square . . . he had blocked his Bishop and couldn't Castle . . . You know, if you are a chess player, the desperate feeling that comes with a blocked Bishop . . . Look down any chess room for a man who's hands are clenched and you'll know that he can't Castle.

So it was not still life for Letherby, and for me, perhaps after awhile I began to feel that it was perhaps just a little *too* still . . . The players moved so little . . . they spoke so seldom, and so low . . . their heads so gray under the light . . . especially, I noticed, a little group at tables in the left-hand corner.

"They don't seem to talk much there," I said.

"No," Letherby answered without even turning his head, "they're blind. Pawn to Queen's Four."

Blind! Why, of course. Why not? Blind people, I realized, play chess as easily as any other people when they use little pegged boards for it . . . Now that I looked I could see—the aged fingers lingering and rambling on the little pegs.

"You take the Pawn?" said Letherby.

"Yes," I said and went on thinking about the blind people . . . and how quiet they all were . . . I began to recollect a play that was once in New York—people on a steamer wasn't it? People standing at a bar . . . and you realized presently they were all dead . . . It was a silly idea, but somehow the Long Room began to seem like that . . . at intervals I could even hear the ticking of the clock on the mantel.

I was glad when the waiter came with a second glass of Madeira. It warmed one up . . .

"That man seem's a wonderful waiter," I said.

"Fred?" said Letherby. "Oh, yes, he certainly is . . . He looks after everything—he's devoted to the club."

"Been here long?"

"Bishop to Bishop's Four," said Letherby . . . He didn't speak for a little while. Then he said, "Why practically all his life—except, poor fellow, he had a kind of tragic experience. He put in ten years in jail.

"For what?" I asked, horrified.

"For murder," said Letherby.

"For murder?"

"Yes," repeated Letherby, shaking his head, "poor fellow, murder . . . Some sudden, strange impulse that seized him . . . I shouldn't say jail. He was in the Criminal Lunatic Asylum. Your move."

"Criminal Asylum!" I said. "What did he do?"

"Killed a man; in a sudden rage . . . Struck him over the head with a poker."

"Good Lord!" I exclaimed. "When was that? In this city?"

"Here in the club," said Letherby, "in this room."

"What?" I gasped. "He killed one of the members?"

"Oh, no!" Letherby said reassuringly. "Not a member. The man was a guest. Fred didn't know him . . . just an insane impulse . . . As soon as they let him out, the faithful fellow came right back here. That was last year. Your move."

We played on. I didn't feel so easy . . . It must have been several moves after that that I saw Fred take the poker and stick its head into the coals and leave it there. I watched it gradually turning red. I must say I didn't like it.

"Did you see that?" I said. "Did you see Fred stick the poker in the coals?"

"He does it every night," said Letherby, "at ten; that means it must be ten o'clock . . . You can't move that; you're in check."

"What's it for?" I asked.

"I take your Knight," Letherby said. Then there was a long pause—Letherby kept his head bent over the board. Presently he murmured, "Mulled beer," and then looked up and explained. "This is an old-fashioned place—some of the members like mulled beer—you dip the hot poker in the tankard. Fred gets it ready at ten—your move."

I must say it was a relief . . . I was able to turn to the game again and enjoy the place . . . or I would have done so except for a sort of commotion that there was presently at the end of the room. Somebody seemed to have fallen down . . . others were trying to pick him up . . . Fred had hurried to them . . .

Letherby turned half round in his seat.

"It's all right," he said. "It's only poor old Colonel Mc-Gann. He gets these fits . . . but Fred will look after him; he has a room in the building. Fred's devoted to him; he got Fred out of the Criminal Asylum. But for him Fred wouldn't be here tonight. Queen's Rook to Bishop's Square."

I was not sure just how grateful I felt to Colonel Mc-Gann . . .

A few moves after that another little incident bothered me, or perhaps it was just that my nerves were getting a little affected . . . one fancied things . . . and the infernal room, at once after the little disturbance, settled down to the same terrible quiet . . . it felt like eternity . . .

Anyway—there came in through the swinging doors a different kind of man, brisk alert, and with steel blue eyes and a firm mouth . . . He stood looking up and down the room, as if looking for some one.

"Who is he?" I asked.

"Why that's Dr. Allard."

"What?" I said. "The alienist?"

"Yes, he's the head of the Criminal Lunatic Asylum . . . He's a member here; comes in every night; in fact, he goes back and forward between this and the Asylum. He says he's making comparative studies. Check."

The alienist caught sight of Letherby and came to our table. Letherby introduced me. Dr. Allard looked me hard and straight in the eyes; he paused before he spoke. "Your first visit here?" he said.

"Yes . . ." I murmured, "that is, yes."

"I hope it won't be the last," he said. Now what did he mean by that?

Then he turned to Letherby.

"Fred came over to see me today," he said. "Came of his own volition . . . I'm not quite sure . . . We may not have been quite wise." The doctor seemed thinking . . . "However, no doubt he's all right for awhile apart from sudden shock . . . just keep an eye . . . But what I really came to ask is, has Joel Linton been in tonight?"

"No . . ."

"I hope he doesn't come. He'd better not . . . If he does, get someone to telephone to me." And with that the doctor was gone.

"Joel Linton." I said, "Why he's arrested."

"Not yet . . . they're looking for him. You're in check."

"I beg your pardon," I said. Of course I'd read—everybody had—about the embezzlement. But I'd no idea that a man like Joel Linton could be a member of the Chess Club—I always thought, I mean people said, that he was the sort of desperado type.

"He's a member?" I said, my hand on the pieces.

"You can't move that, you're still in check. Yes, he's a member though he likes mostly to stand and watch. Comes every night. Somebody said he was coming here tonight just the same. He says he's not going to be taken alive. He comes round half past ten. It's about his time . . . that looks like mate in two moves."

My hands shook on the pieces. I felt that I was done with the Chess Club . . . Anyway I like to get home early . . . so I was just starting to say . . . that I'd abandon the game, when what happened happened so quickly that I'd no more choice about it.

"That's Joel Linton now," said Letherby, and in he came through the swing doors, a hard-looking man, but mighty determined . . . He hung his overcoat on a peg, and as he did so, I was sure I saw something bulging in his coat pocket —eh? He nodded casually about the room. And then started moving among the tables, edging his way toward ours.

"I guess, if you don't mind," I began . . . But that is as far as I got. That was when the police came in, two constables and an inspector.

I saw Linton dive his hand towards his pocket.

"Stand where you are, Linton," the inspector called . . . Then right at that moment I saw the waiter, Fred, seize the hand-grip of the poker . . .

"Don't move, Linton," called the inspector; he never saw
Fred moving toward him . . .

Linton didn't move. But I did. I made a quick back bolt
for the little door behind me . . . down the little stairway
. . . and down the other little staircase, and along the corridor and back into the brightly lighted hotel rotunda, just
the same as when I left it—noise and light and bellboys, and
girls at the newsstand selling tobacco and evening papers
. . . just the same, but oh, how different! For peace of mind,
for the joy of life—give me a rotunda, and make it as noisy
as ever you like.

I read all about it next morning in the newspapers. Things
always sound so different in the newspaper, beside a coffee
pot and a boiled egg. Tumults, murders, floods—all smoothed
out. So was this. *Arrest Made Quietly at Chess Club,* it said.
*Linton Offers No Resistance . . . Members Continue Game
Undisturbed.* Yes, they *would,* the damned old gravestones
. . . Of Fred it said nothing . . .

A few days later I happened to meet Letherby. "Your
application is all right," he said. "They're going to hurry it
through. You'll get in next year . . ."

But I've sent a resignation in advance; I'm joining the
Badminton Club and I want to see if I can't get into the Boy
Scouts or be a Girl Guide.

III

IMPERVIOUS TO WOMEN

"I LOOK on myself," said Baffy Sims, "as a man impervious to women." He wasn't really a man; he was a fourth year undergraduate. But it's often hard to tell them apart.

He said this to me one afternoon on the campus just after lectu.es, but of course I'd heard Baffy Sims say it ever so many times before. Indeed, it was part of a set of fixed ideas; that he was impervious to women; that women were after him; but that they couldn't get him. He always felt and said that a fellow had to be pretty careful. He kept away from clergymen's houses, full of daughters, and never went to teas, lawn parties, nor any fool stuff of that sort. No, sir! Not for him. In fact, that was why we called him "Baffy" Sims, because he used to say that he wished he could go up and live in Baffin Land where there were no women.

All men, as they get old, say things over and over. Sims started young. So we called him "Baffinland" Sims, and then just "Baffy." You know how names get stuck on a fellow at college and stay there. No, no, never mind telling me about the funny ones you remember from your own college. Keep that for another treat.

At any rate this was the afternoon of the evening when Baffy was to read his paper to the Physico-Mathematical Society on the *Natural Inferiority of Women*.

"Be sure to come," he said. "I've got the paper nearly finished. It's a corker. I may give it to the *Atlantic*."

"Oh, don't give it," I said. "Make them pay for it."

"Well, anyway," he said, "it's a corker."

Just then there came scurrying to us such a pretty girl, with a great armful of books tied up with a string. You and I would have noticed at once her beautiful violet eyes, but of course a fellow like Baffy wouldn't see them.

"Baffy!" she said, "I've just caught you in time! Look, I'm going out with Walter to play golf, so you take these books and sling them in at my house as you go by. Tell mother I'll be late . . . If mother's not there, go round to the back door and knock twice and Dinah'll come . . . That's good of you, Baffy."

She was off, leaving Baffy standing there with the armful of books.

"Who," I said with enthusiasm, "is that beautiful girl? Did you notice her eyes—"

"Eyes, hell," he said. "I'm impervious to that sort of thing. That's Pinkie Mordaunt, and I don't go past her house and she knows it. It's half a mile across the park. I told Mrs. Mordaunt last week to tell Pinkie I wouldn't take her books home any more."

"And what did she say?"

"I don't think she quite understood. She said to just give them to Dinah without coming to the front door at all . . . and look now today, with my paper to finish . . . Oh, well, come along . . ."

We had hardly got started when another college girl came fluttering to him. "Baffy," she said, "didn't you hear me call? I was hunting you all over the campus." She handed him a long envelope or rather she stuffed it under the string of Pinkie's books. "Here they are," she said. "I can't work the damn things."

"Quadratics, Dulcie?" said Baffy. Of course he was a real mathematician and could sense an equation even through an envelope.

"I don't know what the hell they are," Dulcie said. "They're what he gave us today."

A college girl always calls her professor simply "he." Some of them are not, but that's what they call them.

"I've got to hand them in at nine tomorrow. You're certainly a real sport, Baffy." "I'm not," Baffy began angrily, but she was gone.

Things never happen singly, or even doubly. So I knew that when I saw a third girl with a bulldog on a leash that there was still more coming for Baffy.

"Lucky meeting you, Baffy," she said.

"I can't take him, Anastasia," he said.

"Yes, you can," she protested. "I want to play tennis with Billy Hyde and I've just no time to take Churchill home . . ."

"Look here, Anastasia, the last time I took Churchill . . ."

"Don't be silly. Last time he hadn't been fed properly— no wonder he bit that boy—anyway Churchill's like that . . . Take him!" she said. And he did.

So that was that.

I'm not awfully keen on bulldogs. Oh, they're faithful! I admit it—and quiet; a bulldog never bites. Oh, no—but I had to go another way anyway so I left Baffy with the dog.

But Baffy got even with them that night at the Physico-Mathematical Society when he read his paper on the *Natural Inferiority of Women*. They said it was a scorcher; and, mind you, they're accustomed in that society to scorch something every week—Monarchy, Christianity, God—things like that. I understand that Baffy showed that women lacked not only brains, but also leadership. In fact he didn't leave them a leg to—or, well, no, that's not exactly the metaphor. I won't say that.

Such was Baffy Sims path at college, impervious, as he said, to women. Not that there was anything mean-spirited about him. I don't imply that for a minute . . . And, of course, he couldn't help it if he knew a lot of girls and if they all called him Baffy. You see, his family had been in the city for ever so long and were well off and knew everybody. So of course the girls paid no attention to Baffy being impervious to women. To them he was just Baffy Sims.

Being well off, life was easy for Baffy in the material sense. He slid easily through Arts and through Law, a subject beyond the range of women, and slid easily as a barrister into a law business, since there was enough family and estate business to start it anyway . . .

But his views never changed . . .

"I've always felt impervious to women," he would say, "ever since I was a boy at college." He'd forgotten about being a man there . . .

But he was a pleasant fellow and life used him easily. Some people, clergymen's wives, said that it was a pity he hadn't married and that they must ask him up to tea . . . So you see there was something in his apprehension after all.

Anyway, his law practice opened out in pleasant and comfortable surroundings as I can testify.

"Come down and see my new offices some day," he said. "I've got everything running fine."

"It'll have to be early in the morning," I said.

"Early as you like," he answered, "or come down with me at nine-thirty."

So the next morning we arrived at the office—a pretty handsome place, I could see at the first glimpse through the open door—at 9:30 A.M. But Mrs. Murphy was still there. You know who Mrs. Murphy is—she's that big woman with the scrubbing pail and brush who is always in a law office before it opens—at her biggest because she's always on all fours and seen from the southwest . . .

"I can't let yez in yet, Mr. Sims," she said. "I've another half hour before I can let you have the office . . . Such a litter, such a dust. Now yous wait outside, half an hour, mebbe . . .

"No, no, Mrs. Murphy," said Baffy, "never mind it now. It'll do fine as it is . . ."

"I might give the offices a touch-up after five," suggested Mrs. Murphy.

"Yes," said Baffy, "that's the idea," and I heard the rustle of a dollar bill passing to Mrs. Murphy, where all rustle ended . . .

"Yes, five o'clock."

"A fine woman," said Baffy as we went into his luxurious offices and sat down. "A fine woman—devoted to her work. Do you know that this is the third morning running that she's been working away over time like that . . . of course, a woman in that class accepts leadership. That woman looks to me . . ."

"She does," I said.

Baffy had hardly begun to show me the office fittings, the law books all in a row—the charm which even law has when young—when the new telephone sounded on the new desk . . .

"Yes, Miss Macarty," said Baffy . . .

"Yes . . . can't come to the office this morning, yes . . ."

"Why, certainly, Miss Macarty; yes . . ."

"Yes . . ."

"Your father's foot? Miss Macarty, why, yes, Miss Macarty . . ."

"Much wiser, yes—take him to Muskoka, yes . . ."

"No, Miss Macarty . . ."

"Back Monday, yes, Miss Macarty, yes . . ."

"Your golf kit? . . . Get it at your house, yes, and send it to Muskoka . . . I prepay it? Yes, yes. See you Monday —good."

"Miss Macarty," he explained, "my secretary. It's her father's gout again. He's a martyr to it. She won't be down this morning because of it. I'm sorry; I'd like you to have met her. A fine girl, and I will say, devoted to her work, never misses—except of course for a thing like this . . . She's her father's sole support outside of what he has of his own."

"And what about his gout?"

"Wretched business, isn't it? Ever had it? Terribly painful . . . comes in sudden attacks . . ."

"And he's got it again?"

"No," said Baffy, "not yet. She wants to forestall it, but it's coming on; she feels it. Often she knows it before he does. Two weeks ago she had to rush him to Preston Springs for the week-end. Last week she rushed him to the Buffalo Races, just in time to ward off an attack. Today she's going to try to make Muskoka—the new hotel there—just in time. That's why she wants me to get her golf kit and send it by express . . . I must remember . . ."

Mrs. Murphy appeared at the door.

"Them ladies," she said, "is downstairs . . ."

"Tell them I'll come and bring them up," said Baffy hurriedly. "Now I'm sorry,—"

"Clients?" I said. "I'll get right out."

"No," he answered, "not exactly . . . It's the Women's Auxiliary Bazaar . . . they're bringing tickets . . . They want me to take a block of two hundred . . . women always imagine that men have more leadership in getting tickets—in fact they said so yesterday . . . Perhaps you'll buy one . . ."

"What's it for?" I asked.

"I don't know," he answered. "Some damn thing."

I saw quite a lot of Baffinland Sims that winter. He was prospering, as he deserved to do, good fellow, and life, except for his silly "impervious" fad, was all bright in front of him. He went out quite a lot into society. I'll never forget the speech he made at Pinkie Mordaunt's wedding, a speech on behalf of bachelors—I wish I could remember it; it was darned good . . . But mostly he went to bachelor gatherings, stag parties. In fact, that was when he founded the U.B.F., the United Bachelors Front, for resisting to the last man. The girls called it—or, well, you can't repeat what girls call that sort of thing.

So there was Baffinland Sims all headed straight for everlasting bachelordom. To think how easily such things end and break! Who could have imagined it all over by that next June? You could? Well, yes, but I mean who else but yourself?

Anyway, you know what the month of June is—all green and soft, all trees and garden and flowers—and every city suburb as fresh as a leafy forest . . . You know what June is;

now take a June garden party, under the trees out on a big lawn . . . in one of those lovely big houses where the city ends and the country begins. Fill in tables scattered over the grass and sandwiches and jellies, and ices and drinks and bottles . . . and bevies of girls in all the colours of the flowers . . . and men in soft flannels—if you want a man to look a real man put him in soft flannel, or loose wool—people moving about in little knots and then untieing the knots to move somewhere else. By that means, you see, you get a drink here and then another drink there . . . and nobody counts them . . . Put in, of course—I was forgetting it—a band, seated around under a big tree and playing while the people move round and have drinks, and then the people stop moving and the band have drinks, and so on. You know what a garden party is on a lawn in June! Does a chicken sandwich ever taste so well? Does a cut of cold ham ever look more enticing? Pop! Bang! God bless me! Champagne! Well! Here's luck!

And mind you it wasn't in *aid* of anything either . . . No, sir.

Well, Baffinland Sims was at the garden party, because he liked to go to that sort of thing. Just to laugh at it . . . It amused him.

So while he was at the height of his amusement at it, I was walking with him through the grounds, and he stopped all of a sudden and clutched my arm and said,

"Who is that marvellous looking girl?"

I didn't see any marvellous looking girl so I said, "Where?"

"There, in white, beside the end of that table!"

I looked and there wasn't any marvellous looking girl. I

mean, there was only Molly Sheppardson. I'm not saying anything against Molly but you'll understand what I mean when I say that that's what it was, just Molly Sheppardson; only her. Molly's all right; a little large, you might say and, at a guess, going to be larger—you know the kind, the girls I mean. So I said,

"It's Molly Sheppardson." Of course, I didn't "only" to him. "I'll introduce you if you like."

"Do," he said, and then, "just a minute," and he began to fumble with his tie, and dust crumbs off himself that weren't there . . .

So I took Baffy over and I introduced him . . .

"How do you do?" Molly said; she speaks easily, I will say. "How do you do? Isn't everything beautifully green?"

I could see that Baffinland was impressed. Here was a girl with a real reach of intellect! Her apprehension of greenness was wonderful.

I left them and wandered on to another table, where a girl I knew said, "How beautifully green everything is," and the man with her murmured "Spring . . ." He was a college man and had just come out first at graduation, so he knew. We had a drink together and then some more people came floating along and saying, "How beautifully green everything is, isn't it?"

But as I moved about I kept track of Baffy. I could see that he never left Molly Sheppardson. They were drifting round from table to table, and when I joined them for a minute Molly Sheppardson said to me, "How beautiful the flowers are!" And Baffinland Sims said to me, "Miss Sheppardson has just been remarking how green everything is . . .

I saw them presently drifting away from the tables. Baffinland told me after that he had taken Miss Sheppardson on to look at the old well in the hollow at the bottom of the lawn; he said he didn't want her to miss seeing that. Yes, that would have been awful, wouldn't it, if Miss Sheppardson had not seen that well. But she saw it. I know she did because I watched them both standing there and peering down deep. I think I know what they saw.

Anyway, everybody saw it. It was just as plain as that . . . From the day after the garden party wherever Molly Sheppardson was, there was Baffinland Sims . . . In fact, it's so old a story that its scarcely worth the telling.

Run smooth? Oh, smooth as spring and soft as summer and mellow as Autumn! Except for one slight interference that pulled it up short, or threatened to. Baffy Sims was going to propose to Molly Sheppardson; he knew it and I knew it because he said so. Then, I don't remember whether gradually or suddenly, he was brought up short by doubt whether he was worthy of her! There was the trouble. Think of it; if it turned out that he wasn't worthy of her—and he admitted that he wasn't fit to black her boots—but they were tan anyway . . . "Women," he explained to me while admitting that I wouldn't understand, "women are so much above men, in practically everything that really matters . . ."

However, it was all right. It turned out he *was* worthy. You see, he did propose to Molly—we won't mind details—and after she had said yes, old Mr. Sheppardson, Molly's father—he's a stock broker—looked into the question of what Baffy was worth. He looked into it down town—and when he came up to the house he welcomed Baffy for a son-in-law with tears in his eyes . . . Old Mr. Sheppardson has done business with those tears in his eyes for forty years. If they were there, the thing was all right.

The wedding was certainly happy . . . The United Bachelors tried to raise a laugh at the wedding breakfast . . . Poor Simps! What did Baffy care!

The proof of it was that the marriage went on being happy . . . There was no story, no tragedy about it. After they were married I happened to be away from the city for some years but I heard all about it,—about their wonderful house in the suburbs, and the children, and Mrs. Sheppardson coming to live with them, and Molly—that's Mrs. Sims—being Head of the Women's Morning Musical (she made Baffy secretary) and President of the Women's Afternoon Dietetic, and the Women's Evening Endeavor, with Baffy as Honorary Vice President of each of them.

So when I returned to the city very naturally Baffy invited me out to his house to dine, and by good fortune it was again the month of June and the lovely place all at its best.

"You remember my wife," said Baffy proudly, as we shook hands. There was indeed plenty to be proud of—at least three sizes larger. "How beautifully green everything is," said Mrs. Sims.

Before dinner Baffy took me up to his "den" for a cigarette —the cutest little den you ever saw—his wife arranged it— away off up on the top of the house under the eaves—it used to be a pigeon house. That's where he smokes. Isn't that a good idea? It keeps the tobacco clear out of the house . . .

We went down again after the cigarette.

"The children," said Baffin, as the five little girls trouped

in to shake hands—Delia, Belia, Phelia—no, I can't remember their names. Anyway, names like that. Perhaps there weren't five; it may have been four or six—nice little things, all so neat and pretty—and the oldest one said to me, "The flowers are lovely, aren't they?"

Then Baffy said, "My mother-in-law, Mrs. Sheppardson— and my wife's aunt, Miss Copperfax"—then he turned to his wife and asked, "Is great-grandmama coming down?"

"Not till after dinner," said his wife.

"I'm sorry," said Baffy and he explained. "My wife's grand-mother, old Mrs. Sheppardson, lives with us . . . she's eighty-eight and just as bright as ever but she seldom comes down to dinner. All she takes in the evening is brandy and water and biscuits, and as my wife never likes any drink served in the dining room, we just send it up to her."

As he spoke, I saw a maid moving away with a decanter on a tray!

"Hey! Stop!" (I thought).

IV

THE JONES'S ENCHANTED CASTLE

("Behold, a cheerful heart can deny adversity and cast out fear."—St. Paul, the Archbishop of Canterbury and Field Marshal Goebbels.)

. . . So WHEN the cheque was made out, the other boys at the club said it was up to me to take it round to Jones. "Other boys" sounds funny, doesn't it? But you can't exactly write "other old men." You see, I'd known Jones about the longest, indeed ever since he and I were at school at the old Upper Canada on King St. Some of them had only known him about twenty years. So they said I'd have to take the cheque and give it either to Jones or to Bess.

I went round right away that same evening. It wasn't yet late.

Jones lives in an enchanted castle, but you wouldn't know it was enchanted if you didn't know Jones and the strange light that burns in him. You'd think the house just one of those old left-behind houses that stand in the old, left-behind streets of Toronto, with ragged palings and half-withered trees.

When I reached it in the half-darkness, there were Jones and Bess at the paling's gate, evidently just coming home. "Come on in," said Jones, cheerily; who wouldn't be proud to say come on in to a house like that . . .

Inside, it was the biggest, darkest, gloomiest house you ever saw—with no lights in it, till Jones took us up to the big

"study" on the first floor and lit a lamp. He's burning coal oil this winter; it's a softer light, it appears, less trying to the eyes. And now that there are no maids in the house you need so few lights that Jones has cut the electricity clean out—he has, or someone has, anyway.

The "study" is just one of the rooms with enchanted names like that; beside it is "father's library" with more dust and fewer books than any I ever saw. And upstairs there is "mother's bedroom" and "Aunt Annie's room," though they're both dead these thirty years. Similarly on the ground floor there is still the "butler's pantry," with fifty niches for fifty bottles that are not there, nor any butler since the time when "father" gave a dinner to the prime minister, while Jones and I were still at Upper Canada. Jones said the prime minister shook hands with him and said some Latin. So!—a house like that—eh, what? With beautiful palings and lovely trees and a butler and a prime minister, and a library full of law books, who wouldn't be proud of it? No wonder it was enchanted. So it is for Bess, too—or at least, because of Jones and the others.

As a matter of fact the old room looked pretty cheery and comfortable when Jones got a good fire going in the grate. It seems he's burning some of the old law books from the cupboard under the library shelves. They're better than soft coal, it seems, less dust and steadier heat. No coal has come to the house, in fact, since it stopped coming. The books are not the ones father valued. He's just burning the Appendix to the *Journals* of the Legislative Assembly of Canada. Father always meant to burn those anyway and Jones only kept them because he was sure they must be darned good reading if a feller ever got down to them. It seems that he never got down to them—or round to them—I forget which

way you get at *Journals*. Anyway they burn well. Jones is still only at the year 1857 and they go clear to Confederation. How's that, eh? That'll last clean to April. And anyway "grandfather" got them all for nothing. Did Jones ever tell you (oh, yes, he must have) how his grandfather moved the second reading of the Pickerel Fisheries Bill and what Sir John A. said?

. . . Anyway it was pretty comfortable in front of the fire and when Jones said, "I'm sorry I haven't a drop of—," why, there! I had a whole flask of it that one of the boys had shoved into my pocket at the club for Jones. As to soda . . . it transpired at once that in "father's" time no one drank it; they said it spoiled good liquor . . . Well, here's luck, eh?

So, to begin talk, I asked Jones where they had been.

"Over at the University at a lecture," said Jones. "Wonderful stuff! Why weren't you there?"

"I didn't know there was one. Many people there?"

"Oh, yes," he said, "quite a good crowd. It's queer, you know, people don't seem to know about all these lectures over at the college . . . wonderful stuff, too . . . and free, mind you, nothing to pay to hear lectures that are mighty well worth it, and more. What was that one about that we were at last week, Bess?"

"Palaeontology," Bess said, looking up from her knitting in the lamplight—like that, just "palaeontology." Bess never wastes words. She lets Jones talk.

"Oh, yes, palaeontology; it means the science of fish; he showed one in a rock. And, do you know, there were only eleven people there, counting Bess; she wasn't exactly *there,* but she came right to the door and then, while I was in, she went over to Mrs. McGinnis's—the professor's wife. It's like

that over there; it's funny; often quite a good crowd almost up to the door, and then a lot break away."

"And what about tonight?" I asked. "Oh, tonight was fine, let me see—counting Bess—she was at the Peterson's—there were twenty-six. Of course it was a subject that would draw, it was on Taxation, the Shifting of Taxation. It was wonderful stuff, a marvellous lecturer."

"A good delivery?" I asked.

"Fine," Jones said, "except his voice—but what I mean is, it was clear over my head, great stuff—in fact I couldn't follow it at all, except some stuff he put on the blackboard. He took a tax and turned it into a line, a curve—and you could watch it get closer and closer to a line and yet never touch it."

"Is that what shifted the tax?"

"I didn't quite catch on to the shifting," Jones said. "It seems, or at least the professor said, that all taxes keep shifting on to the consumer—they heap right up on him till he gets a marginal—now, what did he call it?—oh, yes, a marginal satisfaction, and stops consuming altogether. Wait till I get some more water."

Jones took the jug and started off down stairs with it, stumbling and half stubbing his toe on the worn carpet as he moved off. Everything is worn and everything is wearing out in the Jones's enchanted castle. You see, as Jones says, why bother to put things in shape in the house till the two boys come home. While they're over there, things can stay as they are. Especially as Jones has got the time of their return worked out with great certainty. Eddie, being in the Air, one month after war ends—they'll come first—and John, who is in the artillery, say, a month later. That will give at least a month to have the whole place done over.

So while Jones was down stairs I asked, "Are the taxes paid, Bessie?"

She shook her head.

"Any coal?"

"Another week, anyway."

"There!" said Jones, "fill it up, and let me stir that fire and get another appendix. Here we are, 1859, Vol. I."

I thought that the subject of taxes might give me a start towards the cheque.

"Talking of taxes," I said with an attempt at jocularity, "I suppose you're like the rest of us, right up against it?"

"Oh, no," Jones said, "I'm fine! Right up to date. You see on this house I've always paid, if you understand, just once a year, that is last year for the year before and pay it the next year; this year, I've slipped back a year, but that's only three. I had a notice about it, but all very nice, you know, just something formal about selling the house, etc. But all very nice."

"And the income tax?"

"Ah, that's different. I was getting short there, quite a bit, in fact, well, several years, but this new Ruml plan will clean all that up. Did I tell you?" Jones continued. "I've sent in a plan myself to Ottawa suggesting methods of throwing back taxes forward . . . in fact, that is what I wanted this shifting stuff for . . ."

"What have they done about it?" I inquired.

"Fine," Jones said. "Answered straight back, no delay . . . Referred to File XXOO46 in case I wanted to write further . . . think of the trouble they take, assigning me a personal number like that. And more than that—it seems that the department are going to give my plan every consideration; they said so; they shouldn't really do so much as that. However, if it goes through, it shifts my income tax clear away even without the new Ruml plan; so between the two, I'm in easy street."

"How about your own personal finance?" I said, still feeling for an opening.

"Don't owe a cent . . ."

"I thought you had a mortgage?" I said.

"Oh, yes," he answered, "there's the mortgage. You see, a house like this, as they all told me, carries a fine mortgage— they say, nearly as much as the place is worth. But I never count the mortgage as it is a fixed item. I meant that we have no debts."

"We owe the *bills* . . ." Bess said, still knitting.

"Ah, the bills," Jones answered. "I don't mean *bills*. I was talking of *debts*. The bills—"

"The grocer—" said Bess—"two years."

"You'd hardly count the grocer's account as a bill," said Jones. "Of course, I am not counting things like the grocer and the coal and that; and I must say they've all been awfully decent about it. Why, the coal man the other day, the head man, came right up himself to ask if there was anything I could suggest, and when I said I couldn't he said he couldn't . . . Then of course some of these bills are not new ones at all—they're old bills."

"The doctor's account," said Bess, "goes back to when the boys were at school."

"Exactly," said Jones. "You'd hardly count that, especially with the doctor an old friend. Just now, of course, things are a little muddled, I'm really just waiting till, well, till the boys are back. Everything will all come right then; won't it, Bess?"

"Everything," Bess said, and went on knitting.

"As a matter of fact," Jones continued, "I got, or rather Bess did, a most comfortable little windfall a month ago—money paid out of the remains of her mother's estate—you'd forgotten all about it, eh, Bess? But perhaps, you heard of it?"

"No," I answered. Nor had I, or not since I gave the cheque to Bess at the back door a month ago.

On a pretext of Jones's foot, I let Bess show me out. Down below at the door, I gave her the cheque.

"This," I said, "is from the estate."

She may even have believed me; after all, enchantment is enchantment.

V

MR. ALCORN IMPROVES HIMSELF

*(Each of us by taking thought can add one cubit to his stature.
. . . The New Testament. Revised Version.)*

MY FRIEND Alcorn is improving himself. I don't mean just
at this minute; I mean, that is the main thing in his life,
improving himself. He begins improving himself first thing
in the morning and gets as far as he can with it by night.
If you happen to know Alcorn, don't get facetious about it
and say there's lots of room for it, or something of the sort.
That's too easy. Sandy, scrubby and about half bald, Alcorn
isn't much to look at; and he cracks his knuckles, all his joints
look reversible and he wears a shiny old black tail coat of
the kind that other people gave up about 1890. Of course,
it's hard going to improve him. That's the virtue of it; it's
like a ploughman stubbornly breaking rough land. It's like
those bees that that Frenchman used to write about—what was
his name? Fabre! Of course—I'd forgotten it. Anyway one of
these bees would go out on the empty, burnt, rocky waste
near Fabre's little cottage—well, you know Dordogne; we all
do—nothing but scrub and cactus and glaring sun—and Fabre
would sit for hours, often all day, watching that bee make—
I forget what it made. But it shows what industry can do.
Fabre, they say, made quite a lot, too. . . .

But that's neither here nor there. I am talking of Alcorn
and what he looked like. And don't get the idea that I want
to make a pathetic figure out of him. He isn't pathetic, and

anyway, if he had been he would have bought a twenty-five cent book, *How to Cast out Pathos,* and got rid of it. Oh, no, he's just ordinary. Don't ask me what he *does,* apart from improving himself. I know he does something because there is always a good deal of ink on him late in the day. I frequently see him coming up in the street car in the quieter hours, always reading a little book, a manual of something, but never the same one; and I often see him in the Public Library, changing a book, and I see him in the Art Gallery and at any picture exhibition, studying a catalogue.

You see, if a man's going to improve himself he needs books and catalogues all the time.

If you are the kind of person who would like to get a few hints on the matter, I must tell you that to improve yourself you've got to begin early in the day; in fact, you start by sitting up in bed and taking three deep breaths—*one—two—three*—it's better to count them. That clears the trachea. Did you know it? And after that three quick movements of the neck, quick and snappy. That gives a knock to the anthrax.

The idea of the early morning stuff—here I am merely quoting Alcorn—is to clear the head. The great aim of the first part of the day, the bathroom exercise, the quiet walk, is to get the head absolutely clear. Avoid *thinking,* Alcorn says. It might hold the head back. He tells me that often when he comes in at nine—or rather, anywhere between nine and nine-five—his head is so clear that it just feels empty.

It is either then, or before going out (it doesn't much matter) that it is well to put the eyes under cold water for about five minutes. Alcorn says "the eyes"—not *his* eyes—because he always looks on himself as made of adjustable parts. There are "the eyes" and "the ears" and "the joints."—He himself is just the humble total, not half so important as the ones like diaphragm (be mighty careful with that) and the aesophagus . . .

Still, that's just the start. The main effort is directed at the mind.

Most of the improvement of Alcorn's mind is done out of little manuals, all short and snappy. They have to be quick—*Swedish in Ten Lessons. Spanish in Ten Minutes*—things like that. Anything called a Digest hits him where he lives, or it used to till he found that you could get *Digest of the Best Digests*. "You get it all," he said.

He seems always absorbed in that sort of stuff,—not exactly deeply, but like Fabre's bees, busily. *The World's Great Poetry in Five Pages . . . The World's Great Two-Cent Dramas . . . Religion* (Five Cents) *. . . Outline of the Outlines of Wells' Outline.*

But these rapid studies are intermingled with the real stuff, the solid serious study of the world's greatest and hardest literature. That is what takes Alcorn to the Public Library, with his last book under his arm, waiting for his new one. You will see him handing in Newton's *Principia* to get out Descartes' *Discourse on Method*. "Great stuff!" he would say for each of them. He told me that Kant's *Critique of Pure Reason* was about the biggest stuff he's struck. It took him all Sunday afternoon to read it. He had out Rawlinson's *History of Babylon* on Thursday and was back with it on Friday. "The real thing!" he said.

One peculiarity is that Alcorn's activities keep varying. You can never know what particular line of self-improvement he is at; you have to fit conversation to it as best you could.

Thus I noticed one day that as soon as he sat down in the

street car beside me he began asking most solicitously about my health.

"How've you been keeping?" he said, looking up sideways into my face, with artificial interest. "All right," I said.

"No difficulty with sleep? No insomnia? And I suppose you digest things all right?"

Then I remembered that there was a new book out called *How to Win Friends,* and I remembered that it said, "Always express a solicitous interest in your friends' health." That came, I think, in *Lesson One.*

Another section of Alcorn's self-improvement is done in picture galleries and art exhibitions. He never misses one.

"You see," he likes to explain, in accounting for his presence in such places, "I don't enjoy pictures, that is I *do,* but I don't naturally. But I enjoy trying to enjoy them. That's why I like this exhibition; it seems to me the best we've had for years. There's nothing, or practically nothing, here that I can understand. But I'm working on them. That's why I like this new kind of Catalogue, with little notes about the pictures.

"You know there are lots here that a man likes to study. They don't mean anything to me; I can't get them; now take this one—*Man with Bucket*—of course I get the bucket but the man looks just a blotch—to *me,* that is. I imagine that the merit of it is in the *composition.* Aha!" he continued, turning over the leaves of his catalogue, "*No. 171. Man with Bucket; The artist here attempts a daring composition to convey the sensation of a bucket.* I'm getting it all right; I *knew* that was a composition."

Music he tries also, but sparingly. "Were you at the Symphony Orchestra last night?" I asked. "Oh, yes," Alcorn answered, "I never miss; I just like to sit there and close my eyes and drink it in." But on the whole music beats him. But he loves a street piano and that hurts his feelings.

That's the way I have known Alcorn, like that, ever so long, year in, year out . . . no better, no worse.

Yet here is a strange thing. The kind of odd acquaintance, something between habit and friendship, such as I have had for years from my chance meetings with Alcorn, is a thing one gets unconsciously to value—and you never know it till you lose it. So it was with me when recently I all but lost—all but, not quite—my intercourse with Alcorn.

It was no fault of mine. Somebody gave him as a present my latest book (never mind the title; I'm not advertising), and there he was in the street car tapping the book wrapped up in his pocket.

"I'm looking forward to a great laugh," he said. "Oh, boy!" And then he dipped back behind his spectacles into his *Key to Babylonian Chronology* . . .

"Yes, sir," he said, next day. "I'm looking forward to that book of yours; I couldn't get at it last night, but the first night I have I'm going to get right down to it."

A week later, he said he was keeping the book to take to the Laurentians and have a real laugh, "Eh what?"

After that he nearly took the book to Three Rivers, you know how dull it is there—just the spot, eh, to get right into a book, deliberately, and just sit and chuckle. Three Rivers didn't work—it's a hard place to chuckle in. . . . Then he talked of keeping the book for the holidays. Of course, I didn't mind; I'm used to it; if people *buy* a book they read it, rather than feel stung. But if you give it to them, they don't . . .

Then one afternoon I saw Alcorn slipping into Car No. 65

when I got into Car No. 14. I knew that he was trying to avoid me and that I must do something.

So one day a little later I took care to meet him and I said, "Alcorn, here's a little book for you. Send me that one of mine that you were reading as I'm out of copies, and you take this instead."

"What is it?" he asked.

I showed him the cover. He read out the title. *The Witticisms of* . . . *of* . . . I don't quite see it—these spectacles—"

"*The Witticisms of Hierocles,*" I said, completing the title for him. "It's Greek humor, the oldest there is. You see it's in Greek on the page, but there are little notes that explain each joke. See this page—"

"Oh, boy!" said Alcorn, his spectacles glittering . . .

Our friendship was all set again.

VI

CLOUDS THAT ROLLED BY:
MR. ALLDONE'S AWFUL DAY

("I feel ashamed now to think of the things we used to worry over . . ." Soliloquy of Any Old Man, followed by "What the devil's wrong with this coffee?")

MR. ALLDONE always spoke of it afterwards as "Black Friday." But even in old age he hardly cared to talk about it, except for an hour at a time. Some of us can remember him still; a man of character, Mr. Alldone—you could see it in the sweep of square firm head, suggesting something inside it, or near it, and the firm jaw, always shut unless open.

The scene is in Toronto—not the Toronto that you know but the Toronto of the 'seventies that some of us can still remember; the Toronto of the jingling horse cars, of the young chestnut trees, of Carlton Street as the end of the town with the farms beginning on Bloor St.

Mr. Alldone sat reading his morning paper, his breakfast just done, and one eye out of the bow window to watch for the approach of the horse car. Its appearance was always the sign for getting his hat and cane, kissing his wife good-bye and going out and stopping it.

"It's six minutes late again," he murmured. (Pretty hard on a man, morning after morning to wait anything from three to six minutes.) Then as he looked back at his newspaper a sudden spasm appeared on Mr. Alldone's face.

"What is it, Edward?" asked his wife. "Is it the war news?"

He shook his head. "That's bad enough," he said, "but listen to this:

"World to End in Five Thousand Years!"

"In five thousand years!" gasped Mrs. Alldone. Ella Alldone was a courageous woman, but the brutal suddenness of the thing for the moment struck her down . . . What about the children's education?

Alldone, controlling his voice as best he could, read on:

"Speaking last night in Glasgow, at the Royal Geological Association, Lord Kelvin said that the maximum possible duration of the earth was five thousand years!"

The same unspoken thought overwhelmed them both. If that was the maximum what about the minimum?

"But why should *he* know?" asked Mrs. Alldone, her woman's instinct fighting even the inevitable.

"He's in the peerage," said her husband.

"The one that makes the soap?"

"No, Scotch Whiskey"—and Mr. Alldone added musingly "They have to look ahead in that business."

Then he looked at the paper again and corrected himself "Wait a minute though. It says about him down below 'Lord Kelvin, formerly Sir William Thompson, is senior professor of Physics at the University of Glasgow'."

"Physic?" said Mrs. Alldone.

"Physics," said her husband. "It includes surgery."

Mrs. Alldone did her best to speak calmly. She was glad the children were already off to school. "How does he think it will end?" she asked.

"Frozen—the temperature will fall to absolute cold, 468 degrees below zero." Mrs. Alldone shivered.

"Or possibly"—Mr. Alldone read on—"burned in a terrific

heat of 6,000 degress Fahrenheit . . ." Mrs. Alldone gasped.

. . . "or, on the kinetic theory of gases, blown into fragments in a sudden explosion."

Mrs. Alldone jumped.

When she could speak more calmly she asked. "Does he say how he knows it?"

"He does. He argues that *the present conjunction of Mercury and Saturn . . .*"

"Yes, yes?"

. . . "*means a continued acceleration of the precession of the equinoxes—in other words an aberration of the whole solar system.*"

Mr. Alldone threw down the paper.

"The damn solar system!" he exclaimed.

"Hush! hush!" his wife protested. She knew that he had always complained of the solar system, and never really trusted it. He had always felt there was a catch in it. In fact, it was a standing complaint of his. "One day," he often said, "we'll see." And now they were going to.

"The car!" cried Mrs. Alldone.

Alldone laid aside his paper, put on his coat and gathered up his things. For once he forgot to kiss his wife good-bye, then remembered it at the door and turned back to her. "Forgive me, Ella," he said, "it's a little hard to get used to it."

Then he stepped firmly out on the street in front of the car and waved his hat in the horse's face. The driver, with a rapid turn of the arm of the new powerful circular handbrake, brought the car to a stop, rivetting it to the track, and bouncing up its six passengers.

"You're late," said Mr. Alldone.

"A little, Mr. Alldone; it's a mean morning. We had to

stop and rub down the horse a few times . . . and we're short-handed; there's only me and Bill on the car this morning."

Mr. Alldone went around to the back and got into the car. "Is your wife not coming?" asked Bill the conductor. "No." "All right, Aleck," he called, "you can start."

The half-dozen passengers moved their feet in the straw and nodded.

"War news looks bad, Alldone," one of them said. The man evidently had not seen the worst.

"Fare, please, Mr. Alldone," said the conductor.

Mr. Alldone handed him two cents.

"Three cents, sir, if you don't mind."

"Three cents!"

"It's gone up, sir . . . they gave six months' notice, you know."

"Good Lord!" said Mr. Alldone, as he paid the extra cent. "What on earth is the world coming to? Three cents!" How long could a man go on like this, three cents here and three cents there! Keep that up a few years and where would you be? An extra cent every morning and every afternoon for 300 days or years—add that up, eh?

At the King Street corner Mr. Alldone and a fellow passenger got out to cross the street. A tattered man with a broom of twigs was sweeping round the mud, this way and that. He touched his hat.

"They're getting awful, aren't they?" said Mr. Alldone. "Something should be done about those fellows, standing there and expecting a cent. Do you know, I heard they investigated one of those fellows at the police court and found that he had made forty cents in a single day!"

"No wonder we pay taxes!" growled the other.

Mr. Alldone went up to his office. He was a broker. In the office was Phillips, his clerk—an ageing man in threadbare black, frail and worn, but able to write a hand like copperplate, for he had once been a clerk in London. There were no machines then.

"The war news is bad, Phillips," said Mr. Alldone.

"Bad sir, very bad," said Phillips, and when he spoke it was with the accent of London and the British army. He'd left his clerkship for the Queen's shilling. Twenty years he'd had. Thin old veterans like Phillips in those days often got fine jobs like what Phillips had, at thirty dollars a month and a holiday every holiday.

"I'm glad they've got Lord Chugsford, sir," continued Phillips. "He knows that hill country."

"This is terrible news, too," said Mr. Alldone, pointing at the item about Lord Kelvin.

"Bad indeed, sir," said Phillips, "I hope I never live to see it."

Mr. Alldone sat down to read the news in detail. Bad, bad it was. As the cable headings put it: *Darkest Day of War. All England Anxious. Courage high. News from the NEPAUL CAMPAIGN. Funds fall a penny-halfpenny*. Then followed the details, plainly and courageously written, as for a people measuring the cost (in pounds, shilling and pence):

Lord Chugsford's entire Force, 300 of all ranks with 20 marines and a rocket gun, have advanced up the Brahmapootra into the Garghai Hills where they have suffered a severe reverse. Sir Dumdum Bullit, who led the advance, reported three men hit, with something or other, and a Highland piper shot through the bagpipes, courageously continuing to play. The forces have fallen back, backwards and forwards.

It was ominous enough. But more ominous still, to the trained intelligence of a broker, was the brief announcement that the Funds had fallen three cents! For the moment all thought of the end of the world was banished from Mr. Alldone's mind. This thing was nearer. If London had fallen three cents, what was happening in New York? Wall Street must be in a ferment.

"The ticker! The ticker!" he called to Phillips. "How's New York?"

There were no telephones then. But the circular telegraph tape called the ticker carried the stock news—as long as it stayed in order.

"It broke yesterday afternoon, sir," Phillips said. "But I've sent Billy over to the telegraph office for the bulletins. He won't be—"

In fact, Billy, the office boy, arrived at that moment.

Bad news, brief but bad. New York Central down two cents, Boston and Albany a cent and a half, the Erie Canal up one point but the Baltimore Canal down two.

But bad news never comes singly. A messenger appeared with an envelope. Alldone recognized the handwriting of the chairman of the Stock Exchange and tore the note open.

It read:—

Dear Alldone: Early morning telegrams have brought a flood of offers and orders—at least a dozen, certainly ten—showing a total collapse of values, Grand Trunk two cents, Great Western one cent, Goderich Ditch Canal a cent and a half, with Manitoulin Fish thrown on the market. Under the circumstances I write to you and to the other seven members of the exchange to say that on my own authority I am closing the Exchange. I am leaving the key with Peter, the bartender at Clancy's.

Alldone got through the morning in the office as best he could; later on he could scarcely remember how. Once or twice he sent Phillips along the street and got back the report that the Exchange rooms were closed but that people were selling shares outside on the sidewalk at, literally, whatever they could get. Phillips had seen Grand Trunk sold five cents down, and Manitoulin Fish refused at any price. There was great gloom, he said, on the street. News of the disaster in Nepaul was by this time all over town. Work had practically stopped. People stood silent in little groups, or walked away and talked to themselves.

At half past twelve Alldone said, "I shall go out now and get a bite of lunch, Phillips—not that I can eat it—I'll be right back, probably within an hour."

Lunch, in the Bodega Grill on Leader Lane, had always been one of the pleasant spots in Alldone's day—the bright cosy grill, open glowing coal fires all down one side, chefs in white, waiters in black, sherry in great casks end-on, chops frizzling, everybody talking, blue smoke rising.

All changed today. The patrons of the Bodega Grill sat silent, staring at the newspaper with little more than a nod and a word to a newcomer. Appetite was evidently gone. A man would order a porterhouse steak, sit and look at it, then eat it and get up and go out; or order a chop, toy with it, then read the paper, toy with it again and then finish it.

Even the genial face of the proprietor had exchanged something of its pleasant aspect for the marks of anxiety.

"Three mutton chops, as usual Mr. Alldone?" he asked.

Alldone shook his head. "Two and a half," he said.

"This is the noon paper, sir," said the waiter, as Alldone sat down. "Sherry, sir?"

Alldone nodded. It didn't seem worth while to speak. He'd get it without.

As he drank his sherry, mechanically, and hardly realizing what he was drinking except that it was sherry, Alldone read the latest London dispatches . . .

"The disaster to British Arms in the Nepaul Campaign," says the Times, *"has had a reverberating effect throughout Europe. It is recognized that England has received a blow in her prestige, the one place where she can't stand it. But we are assured that England will not turn her back."* Then followed the leading account. *"Further cable despatches from London only deepened the gloom of what someone has fittingly called England's Darkest Hour. The fall of the Funds by three cents (as before) has led to a general fall of security values averaging anything from one farthing to a penny halfpenny. The Bank of England directors have at once raised the discount rate to ten per cent, gone into the bank and nailed up the door. Lord Gloop, the great financial expert, has said that England is within twelve hours of barter. He said this ten hours ago. Greatest anxiety prevails as to what happens next.*

Alldone had barely finished his chops and followed them with apple pie and doughnuts, more to conserve his strength than because they were included in the price of the chops, when a messenger boy entered with a special news cable bulletin for the proprietor.

"Read it, read it," called several of the men.

The proprietor looked at it, turned a trifle pale and shook his head. "You read it," he said to Mr. Alldone.

Alldone stood up and read the dispatch:

"London, Friday, 3 p.m., Queen Victoria stricken with

attack of gout. Royal Physician, Sir Magnus Alhell in attendance."

There was a gasp from the listeners.

"Sir Magnus has prescribed a complete rest for Her Majesty, urging that she must not open Parliament today; he insists on her taking a pint of burgundy every half hour. If she won't, he will."

There was a chorus of approval. "He will, eh? That's the stuff," they said. Men recognize the true British spirit when they see it.

"Wait a minute," said Alldone, "there's more on the back . . . *He will not be responsible.* That's it."

Well,—there was nothing to do but wait,—wait and hope. But meantime, to all of them must occur the thought, what is Canada doing? Will Canada give no help? Where is Ottawa? Some didn't know.

For Alldone, the afternoon wore away with the same listless waiting. He was glad when the day drew to its end, glad to walk back home without waiting for the horse car, though he could see it not far behind him, glad even to find himself back in his own home.

Then came the first break in the clouds.

His wife was standing in the doorway, waving an afternoon paper. "Look—look!" she called. "Isn't it splendid?"

A moment later, Alldone, his eyes almost dazzled with joy, was sitting reading the latest bulletin from Glasgow:

"LORD KELVIN EXPLAINS. LONGER PERIOD ASSIGNED TO EARTH'S DURATION.

"Lord Kelvin drove to the office of the Glasgow Times to-

*day to explain his statement of yesterday and said that his
estimate of the earth's duration is not five thousand years but
five billion. The error was solely due to a shortage of type in
the printing office, only three naughts being available for this
item. The proprietors of the newspaper at fault have apolo-
gized very handsomely to Lord Kelvin and paid his cab fare
both ways."*

They both sighed with relief! It was good to be back in
the happy old world, with five billion years all their own.

But there were bigger and brighter and happier things still
to come.

They had hardly risen from their simple dinner—a joint
and a fowl—when they heard the newsboy outside in the gathering dusk calling, *"Special, Extra!—War News Extra!"*

Alldone rushed out for the paper—money didn't matter
now—and when he brought it in, read out to his wife in a
voice half choked with emotion but ringing with pride:

*Canada to Britain's Aid: Dominion will send contingent
up the Brahmapootra . . .* Then followed all the glad news
that was making many a home proud that evening:—

*"It is announced from Ottawa that a Canadian War Con-
tingent will be at once sent up the Brahmapootra. The force
will consist of a hundred men, eighty of them trained voya-
geurs, and the rest on snow-shoes. The Prime Minister has
assured the country that none of the expense will fall on
Canada. He is not prepared to say where it will fall, but it
won't be here."*

"Isn't it simply wonderful?" said Ella, as she bent over her
husband and kissed him. Then as she did so, her eye caught
a final stop-press news item along the foot of the paper.

"QUEEN VICTORIA OPENS PARLIAMENT ON ONE LEG."

"Oh, Edward!"—and with that she crossed over to the piano (she was a trained musician), struck the opening chords, and said, "Come, Edward, sing . . . *'God . . . save . . . our gracious . . . Queen'."*

VII

ANGEL POND, LURE OF THE NORTH

("North, I think it is, they call it, where the Sons of Women are Men. . . ." One of those Poets.)

Who should I meet the other evening in the rotunda of the Big Hotel but Charlie Blunt. I knew he'd been "up north" for a year or more; in fact it was the first thing he said. But I could have told it anyway—so could you. You can always tell the fellows just "down from the north" at a glance; that look of perfect physical condition, brown and tanned—well, not exactly *tanned*—dirty? No, I wouldn't just say dirty—but, you know—dark looking—the Indians get it themselves; neatly shaved—I mean, neatly three-quarters shaved—they don't go further in the north; standing square and stocky as if he were on snow-shoes. When Charlie stepped he lifted his feet well up—not to trip over branches.

"Yes," he said, "I'm just down from Angel Pond—that's where our new mine is—down here to buy machinery, and hang it, it's all held up, everything's held up these days—I'll be kicking round six weeks waiting for it."

I saw at once that Charlie was like all the rest of them; no use for any place but the North. You'd think a fellow would be glad to get away from a place like Angel Pond in winter. But, oh no!

"Where is Angel Pond anyway, Charlie?" I asked.

"Angel Pond?" he answered, "well—do you know where God's Lake is?"

"No—"

"Well, it's a long way east of that, anyway. You know Little Jesus River?"

"No—"

" . . . where you portage to All Saints Creek . . ."

"A pretty religious set of names you have up there, Charlie," I said.

"They are," he assented with a laugh. "It was the French who first went through that country in the early days. They're a devout people and they like to give all the rivers and portages their religious names. The idea was that it helped them to get through . . ."

"Is that so?"

"I like it," Charlie went on. "We've tried to imitate it in English on our side of the divide round Angel Pond—we've got Lower Devil River and All Hell Elbow and Beelzebub Rapids. It's a good idea, isn't it? But say," he continued, "come on with me upstairs. There's a bunch of fellers up there in a room that I was just going to join. I guess you know some of them . . ."

There is always a "bunch of fellers upstairs in a room" at the Big Hotel. I think they keep roomfuls of them on purpose. I knew what they would look like before we even started up—a big sitting-room, filled with blue tobacco smoke, a lot of bottles on the tables—a bowl of ice—some lemons (the fellers never use the lemons; they just *order* them)—anyway, lemons, matches, cigars, all those things that go nicely round a whiskey bottle . . .

We got into the elevator, Charlie stepping well over the loose branches as he got in, and up we went, and there the fellers were, just like that. They're always the same; you don't exactly remember their faces, and you don't quite recall their names, but you don't need to . . .

Even if you didn't know them you'd recognize them by their talk. Just as we came in one was saying, "I paid three cents and then like a damn fool I let it go at seven cents." Some one else murmured, "I let it go at eight . . ." and another said, "It was nineteen cents today." People not used to high finance get dazzled with figures like these . . .

But the talk broke off into loud greetings of "Hullo, Charlie . . . Have a Scotch, Charlie! Say When! . . . Here try this one—" and so on.

"How did you come out, Charlie?" asked one of the "fellers." "Is it easy?"

Anyone who knows the speech of the north, understands that doesn't mean how did you *succeed*. It means how did you make your way out of the hundreds of miles of tangled wilderness . . .

"Oh, it's easy," Charlie said. "There's no difficulty with Angel Pond. You can either go by rail to Sioux Lookout and then canoe and portage from there . . . or round from God's Lake to Old Shoes . . . It's only a hundred and fifty to two hundred miles either way. You can do it in a week."

"Are the flies bad in summer?" asked someone.

"Oh, the flies are nothing to us . . . you just smear your face thick with any kind of fat, groundhog fat, skunk's fat—and wrap a heavy veil over your face and slip a leather coat over everything else. They never get you that way . . ."

"Can't you get in by plane?" someone asked.

"Not exactly. The Pond, Angel Pond, itself is too small to land on and the trees are too thick for landing anywhere near. There's Paradise Lake, quite big enough, but it's twenty miles away and some people don't like it . . . they don't care to come that way."

"Don't like it?"

"No, there's a good many wolves through there. Of course, people have the craziest idea about the wolves up north. As a matter of fact a timber wolf has to be mighty hungry before he'll attack anyone—I mean in daytime."

"He would at night?"

"Yes, he might, especially if there's a bunch of them running in the woods together . . . but you can always hear the howls in time . . ."

"Hear the howls?"

"Yes, and get up a tree . . . there's lots of jack pine there, you know, and once you get up in a jack pine, well, there you are."

"Up in the jack pine!" said a fellow.

"Exactly," said Charlie; he took everything literally, "and in the morning they're gone."

Charlie paused a minute and a shadow passed across his face. Perhaps he was hearing the howl of the wolves on a frozen lake in the bush country.

"Have another Scotch, Charlie."

"Thanks," he said, and drank it in that plain straight-forward way they have in the north. That is to say he drank it. Then it was gone.

"People have got," he said, as he put down the glass, "the craziest ideas about the north country."

"It's not really cold, is it?" someone asked. There is always a smart Aleck in a group of "fellers."

"Not as a rule," Charlie said. (He never distinguished jest from earnest; they don't up there; either you mean a thing or it's an insult.) "Not as a rule, certainly not at the Pond.

I've known it, even in January, that the thermometer will get up to fifteen and stay there day after day, never colder."

"Fifteen above zero?"

"Fifteen below . . . of course, I don't say that's usual. More likely you get that for a day or two and then it turns really cold."

"What's the place like anyway, Charlie?" asked a man who this time really wanted to know. "Is there a town? Are there shops? and churches and places?"

"Why, of course," said Charlie, "just like any other place, or pretty nearly. You see, there's the mine—of course we're not producing yet, but we're getting pretty well developed— there's the mine—and, of course, there's the men's quarters —they're all right, the men—most of them. They're Polacks, mostly, but they're all right. They don't speak much English, but that's all right. Well, there's the mine, and quite a few houses, like Dan Clough's, the machine superintendent's, he's down here with me getting machinery. Well there's his house, and quite a few like that . . ."

"A church?"

"Yes, certainly, what do you think we are? There's a church, or at least we've put a building up, a dandy, that we can use for a church—jack pine and tamarack—with open fireplaces and lockers for bottles—we're using it as a sort of club just now because we've no one to preach in it yet . . . the boys play poker in it. We've got electric light and all kinds of modern comforts like, well—electric light and those sort of things . . ."

"Well, what kind of fellers are up there?" persisted the questioner.

"What kind of fellers?" Charlie answered almost angrily. "Why, first class! What would you expect? Some of the fellers are working for the company, and others come through surveying and prospecting. Now you take Freddie de Vere, —he came out from England. Freddie had been at Oxford but he was all right. You'd never notice the difference. Freddie was with us for months and months last year. He brought out money to invest but he lost it."

"In mines?"

"No—just with the boys. He's gone back for more. He has an uncle who is a big English financier—I don't mean a crook, I mean an English financier—Freddie may get him to invest in Angel Pond but this uncle wants to make sure. He wants to be assured first about the question of its being crooked. If he wasn't sure of that he wouldn't put in a cent. The boys are looking forward to Freddie coming back. He was popular . . ."

Then someone asked the question we all had in mind.

"Any women?"

"Women! Why, of course, women, and some mighty nice cultivated women too. Take Mrs. Clough—that's Dan Clough's wife, the machine superintendent; he's down with me now—the *Senora,* we call her . . . she's from Mexico. Her first husband was hanged down there. But that's nothing against *her.* And her present husband, Dan, is A1. So was her second husband, too. Dan knew him in Mexico. He was shot. Then Dan brought her up here. She's a mighty fine woman, cultivated—experienced."

"She must be," remarked a feller. But it went past.

"Then there is Mrs. Macdonough, Sandy Macdonough's wife. He's the government surveyor."

"Scotch?" asked someone.

"He is," said Charlie, "he's from New Brunswick. She's a MicMac. That's why he brought her up. There's quite a little group of women . . . they're all right, too, better than a lot of your darned . . ."

He paused and the shadow fell. It hadn't occurred to him to doubt the merit of those whom they called the "girls" up at Angel Pond.

"Have another Scotch, Charlie," someone said. He drank it.

What was the good of trying to explain the North to a bunch of flats in the city, who had no idea what it's really like . . . it all seems to come out wrong. Charlie Blunt's good-tempered face took on a saddened look.

Charlie, I say, seemed a little discouraged. The shadow had fallen across his face. He took his drink and there was a moment's silence. Then one of the "fellers" just to put him in countenance again, said gently:

"And you hope to get a clergyman there at Angel Pond, presently?"

"Oh, yes," Charlie said, "in fact we have our eye on the very man, if he's not too big for us to swing. You've probably heard of Reverend Irwin?"

No one had.

"We had him, Irwin, down to see us last winter. He's the Bishop of Belcher Islands, they call him the 'Apostle of the North.' Ever heard of him?"

It stuck in my mind that I'd heard of about twenty "Apostles of the North," more than the original crowd, but I couldn't remember this one.

"He's a great feller," said Charlie. "He's a huge, husky-looking man, so big he'd throw any two of us all round. He'd do it, too, mind you in a minute. He's the real thing, that man—no religious stuff, you know what I mean—takes a drink any time, takes a cigar, takes anything. What do you think

that man did? He went the year before last right up among
the Eskimos along the north of the Bay, lived right among
them—just shared everything they had; just took what they'd
got and never asked for anything else . . ."

"Yes. It was their special seal season when they catch the
young seal and have the blubber feasts. The Bishop just sat
right in and ate blubber—more than they could."

"He did, eh?"

"And the year before that he went right across the plains—
You know where the Athabascan Indians have their big annual cariboo hunt east of Lake Athabasca? Well, the Bishop
went and lived with them—just like one of themselves, shared
everything with them, just what they had, food, tobacco—just
one of themselves. That's the season you know, of the cariboo meat feast. He was in that."

"And what did the Bishop come to you for, Charlie?"
asked the smart Aleck.

"He'd run out of chewing tobacco," Charlie answered, "but
he never complained, just started out for three hundred miles
on snowshoes. He'd been with the Mounted Police, near
God's Lake."

"Preaching to them?" someone asked.

"No, helping them to find whiskey . . . often and often
he finds it when no one else can. 'Let me get it,' he says, and
goes out all alone. Well, anyway he ran out of chewing tobacco and he came all the way down to get some at Angel
Pond."

"Did he preach to you at Angel Pond?" we asked.

"He was going to," Charlie said, "he was all set to, but the
way it was—that very Sunday, not knowing he was coming,
they'd arranged to use the church for a big euchre game, so

the Bishop joined in that instead. But he carried out a baptism there right after the game—"

"One of the children?"

"No, there weren't any. It was an old Indian, Musquash Joe—they say he's a hundred and ten years old. The Bishop found he'd never been baptised and baptised him right there . . ."

"In a font?"

"No, with a teaspoon with a little whiskey. He's like that —always finds a way to do a thing. He's a great fellow—" Charlie repeated—"more good than all these high-toned city clergymen put together. He left us to strike right across to Lake Mistassini. The Indians over there—they're Montagnais, you know, and haven't changed since Champlain—hold their dog feast once a year. The Bishop was timing himself for that. You know," said Charlie, "I think a man like that spreads Christianity, gets people to know it, better than all the darned . . ."

But just at that moment another man shoved the door of the room open and appeared in the doorway with a bag in each hand.

"Say, Charlie," he called, "you'll have to hurry. The train goes in fifteen minutes and we can only just make it. I've got the reservations and everything . . ."

"All right," said Charlie, as he rose in a chorus of good-byes and good wishes.

I walked out into the corridor to say good-bye.

"You off back north already?" I said. "I thought your machinery wouldn't be ready for six weeks."

"It won't," he added. "Dan and I (meet our mine superintendent) are taking a trip to Florida."

VIII

COOKING FOR VICTORY

"OH, MRS. BEETON, is it really you? I am so delighted to meet you. How terribly well you look, and—if you don't mind my saying so—how nice and plump. Of course it must be the good feeding."

And with that we sat down to talk in Mrs. Beeton's double drawing-room. It seemed so wonderful to be actually talking to Mrs. Beeton, that famous Mrs. Beeton of Mrs. Beeton's Cook Book. I had imagined that she must have been dead and gone—perhaps cooked—long ago. Yet here she was, sitting in the drawing-room in front of me, and absolutely unmistakable—the full, matronly figure, the dark dress fitting close to what was called in her day the bust, the neatly parted hair, the bangles, the *pince-nez*—oh, Mrs. Beeton certainly, wherever she came from.

"I'm especially glad to meet you now," I went on, "because there are so many things I want to ask you. In war-time, it seems to me, careful cooking and the economy of food would mean a tremendous lot."

Mrs. Beeton gravely bowed her head. "In war-time," she said, "as I frequently tell Mr. Beeton, the services of women are the mainstay of the nation." . . .

"And what does Mr. Beeton say?"

"He doesn't say anything," she said, "I shouldn't wish him to."

"Mr. Beeton, I suppose, must be of great help to you in collaboration?"

"None whatever," she said calmly—"or practically none. Of course he eats everything first, particularly now when there's such a danger of poisoning."

Then to my surprise she called: "Alfred!"

I was aware of something in a dressing-gown shuffling around in the other half of the room and a voice said, "Yes, my dear!"

"Go up and bring me down from my writing-table my *Cooking for War-time*, the 1943 Revision."

I heard something start shuffling up the stairs. Then Mrs. Beeton called, as if by an afterthought.

"Alfred, one minute!"

"Yes, my dear."

"Had you finished what you were eating?"

"Yes, quite finished."

"You ate it all?"

"Virtually, yes, virtually."

"And are you still all right? You are? Then go on up and get the book."

"It is a very interesting experiment," she said. "You see, in war-time it is simply impossible to let people keep their aluminum pots and saucepans merely because they prevent poisoning . . . we need the metal . . . so I have been having Alfred's breakfast cooked in different kinds of cheap metal, to see which are free from poison. This morning I tried galvanized iron. Ah, here he comes with the book . . ."

Mr. Beeton shuffled in, his long Victorian dressing-gown up to his ears. He had a mild face, quite empty.

"Let me introduce Mr. Beeton, my husband," said Mrs. Beeton.

Mr. Beeton came forward with an outstretched hand and a sort of feeble cheeriness.

"I rather think"—he began.

"You don't need to, Alfred," said Mrs. Beeton, "and now run along like a good boy for I have some important business here. Ask Cook for some beans that you are to eat—she knows which ones—"

"And now—" said Mrs. Beeton—"I know just what you're thinking of—war-time recipes. You see, I have been working on it. I have a list of Recipes Directed to the War-Time Effort for conserving the natural food supply by (a) using minimum quantities, (b) using the cheapest ingredients, (c) making things go as far as possible, (d) preserving the flavor, taste and appetizing quality of dishes."

"That's it," I said, "exactly," and I took out a pad and pencil as I spoke—"and I'd like to write some of them down for the newspaper I represent."

"Very good," said Mrs. Beeton and began turning over the leaves of the big book. "Let me see—what shall we try? Now here—*terrapin—tarragon—turtle soup*—do you like turtle soup?"

"I do," I said.

"So do I, very much, in fact I adore it. It's too rich for Alfred but I used to serve it all the time. Let's see what it says. 'Take a fresh turtle, take one gill of old sherry or madeira.' "

"But stop," I said, "I'm afraid there are no turtles on the market now"—

"No, I forgot, of course not—but this, *pâté de foie* sandwiches. 'Take one gill of fine old brown sherry, one ounce of pâté, and a sandwich. Insert the pâté in the sandwich, and drink the sherry before serving.'

"Now that," she said, "would be excellent for war workers in offices, just as a snack, every half hour or so, while waiting for meals. Here's a similar one," she went on, again turning the leaves, "that would be excellent to stave off fatigue. 'Lobster jelly in aspic—take a gill or more of old brown sherry, one cold broiled lobster and a pot of melted aspic. Remove the lobster's claws and dip them in the aspic. Drink the sherry while dipping them.' And now here's something that would be terribly good, I think, for men on active service, especially men at sea, who suffer from lack of appetite . . . it's really delicious. *Quail a la King*—take a pint of Burgundy, one quail, and a few leaves of mace, thyme, rosemary, with either asparagus tips or French *petits pois*."

"Oh, but I'm afraid, Mrs. Beeton," I interrupted, "you had rather mistaken my meaning. I wasn't thinking so much of delicacies, and luxuries and things to tempt the appetite. I was thinking more of plain food for the home, how to cook plain wholesome dishes at a minimum cost."

"Ah, but you should have said so," said Mrs. Beeton cheerfully—and I realized that whatever she might or might not be, she was at least a comfortable, cheerful sort of person, a result, no doubt, of much catering to the male appetite. "Plain food, of course, but that's the very thing we are all most interested in. Let me see . . ." She readjusted her glasses and ran the leaves again through her fingers, muttering the headings as the pages went past . . . plain joints and cuts . . . dog meat . . . meat for the nursery . . . servants' meals . . . feeding cats. "Ah, yes, now this for example— Irish Stew."

Mrs. Beeton sat back triumphantly, her face all smiles, her book poised for reading.

"Irish Stew!" she repeated enthusiastically. "Do you like it?"

"Very much indeed," I said, "and surely that must cost very little."

"Nothing!" said Mrs. Beeton. "Practically nothing, when it's made according to my recipe—just a few simple things and a few ingredients that are found in every kitchen. Now, suppose we work this out together. You check it off with your pencil. Of course, you can alter the quantities if you like. Are you ready? Take about a gill of old brown sherry . . . wait," she said, "we'll judge that by itself; nothing like accuracy. I'll have Cook bring it."

Mrs. Beeton reached out and pulled an old-fashioned bell-rope that hung beside her. To my surprise a cook appeared, looking like Mrs. Beeton herself, just out of an old-fashioned book—the full white apron, the queer white cap.

"You rang, ma'am?" she said.

"I did," said Mrs. Beeton. "I want you to bring about a gill—or no, two gills; we must work it out separately—of sherry."

"The old brown ma'am?" asked the cook.

"Yes, the old brown, and, oh, Cook—just a minute—has Mr. Beeton eaten his beans?"

"Yes ma'am," said the cook, "all but a few."

"Give those to Fido," said Mrs. Beeton.

"I have," said the cook; "she won't touch them."

"H'm," said Mrs. Beeton thoughtfully. "Has Mr. Beeton gone upstairs yet?"

"No, ma'am, he's just sitting there."

"Ah," said Mrs. Beeton cheerfully, "digestion! I always have him sit very still when I'm experimenting. That'll do, Cook, and thank you."

"Now," Mrs. Beeton went on, resuming her cheerful and efficient manner, "the use of sherry in Irish stew is a thing of which many people are ignorant. But it's most economical as the Irish stew goes ever so much further if mixed with sherry . . . indeed you hardly need any stew. Now, try that sherry. Excellent, isn't it?"

The good lady beamed over her sherry glass . . .

"No doubt you agree that a brown sherry is better in any recipe than a dry sherry . . . The only question is whether a gill is enough. However, let's see what follows. *Irish Stew.* Take a dozen eggs."

"A dozen eggs?" I protested. "But surely no one could afford a dozen, and anyway eggs are not in a stew."

"We always mix the gravy, the liquid part first," explained Mrs. Beeton. "Take a dozen eggs, or more as required, and beat them in French Burgundy; stir in bay leaves, rosemary, and a liberal quantity of truffles."

"But surely," I protested again, "no one could have all those things now. What is the meat part?"

"It's economy in the long run," said Mrs. Beeton. "After that come the potatoes and plain vegetables and all that but, if you like, I'll skip that to go right to the meat . . . let me see. Yes, here . . . take a young boiled lamb and throw away all of it but the ribs; dip these ribs in the stew as already prepared and serve with melted butter and anchovy sauce laced with brandy."

But at that moment Cook appeared in the doorway.

"I beg your pardon, ma'am," she said.

"Well," said Mrs. Beeton, "what is it?"

"It's master. He seems took rather bad. He's fallen off his chair."

"Tut, tut," said Mrs. Beeton quietly, "the beans, of course.

But some of our experiments are bound to fail; we must simply persevere and persevere. Cook," she continued, "you must run across the street to the doctor's and ask him to come over, and to bring his stomach pump, the large one . . ."

"And now," she said, turning to me, "I'm afraid I must ask you to excuse me. Illness in the house always depresses me. I shall take a walk. Good morning."

IX

GOOD NEWS! A NEW PARTY!

("The old-time political parties, gentlemen, have had their day. What we need is new life, new energy and, above all, if I may say so, a new Working of the Spirit."—From any soapbox, Halifax to California.)

IT IS a great pleasure—indeed it gives me a thrill—to be able to announce to the public through the kindly medium of this volume that at last the New Party has come! The hope, the promise, contained in such words as those above is fulfilled. The thing is here. I saw its inception. I was present at it myself no later than last night. All that is now needed is to keep it incepted . . .

Now, please, don't ask me for details, for names and places and all that; everything will appear in the full publicity of the newspapers.

It came about this way. I'm not in politics but I have many friends who are—some on one side, some on the other, some on both . . . naturally I hear of the new movements. So when Hoggitt called on the phone to me to come down and join him at the Piccadilly I knew that the big stuff was on.

I found him there at a table and he began to talk, right away and with the greatest enthusiasm, about the new Party. You know Hoggitt. He's all right. He's got a sort of fierce way of talking, but he's all right. He's a big dark fellow and he always seems to be threatening but he isn't—that is, he *is* in a way, but he's all right. Anyway I'd no sooner sat down

than he was talking full speed of the Party—with a sort of in-
spiration.

"It's the real thing," he said, "it's based on human sympathy and equality—where's that damn waiter? We're aiming
at what the old parties never had—social cohesion—I'd like to
fire that fellow—and the right of every man to a voice . . .
gimme that check and don't talk back to me . . ."

He was still muttering at the waiter when we left . . .

"We'll drive along to the meeting," he said.

But, of course, we couldn't get a taxi; we waited—say, we
must have waited four minutes; anyway Hoggitt said, "Oh
come along. There's no use waiting for a taxi; these taxi
fellers just go beyond all limits . . . and *money!* What
they're making now! I don't know what they get, but, by
gosh, a mighty comfortable living, I'll say! It's a scandal."

So we walked. In any case it was only four blocks and I
was glad because it gave Hoggitt a chance to explain to me
all about the new party. I must say it sounded fine—no more
of that miserable intrigue and crookedness of the old parties
. . . things done in the dark . . . no more leaning on the
"interests" for money; just straight honesty. Hoggitt said
that when we got to the hall he'd introduce me to the chairman, but not to pay too much attention to him as they were
going to ease him out. Of course he doesn't know it. They'll
keep him while they still need him. Hoggitt said he's not suf-
ficiently genial—that was it—or, no, I've got it wrong—*too*
genial.

The meeting was in a pretty big hall. There must have
been well over a hundred, most of them smoking and standing round. They looked all right, too. I've been to a good
many political meetings but I couldn't see anything wrong
with them. Some of them looked mighty decent fellers, you

know—educated—not like what you'd imagine at all. It seemed a kind of free and easy crowd. The chairman was just going to the platform so I only had time to shake hands with him, a middle aged looking man, quite well dressed—in fact I couldn't see a thing wrong with him.

Anyway he got up to talk, but they didn't listen much; they went on talking in groups round the room. Hoggitt said that's the way they do; they find they can get through more business if they don't listen. Hoggitt says that's the curse of Washington and Ottawa—one of them; he named quite a few.

The chairman was talking about the name of the party. He said, "Gentlemen, you'll be glad to know we've succeeded in getting a name for our party. You remember last week our difficulty over the proposal to christen the party the Forward Party . . ."

There was noise and applause which Hoggitt explained to me was because some of the members—people of fine old families who'd never moved since they came to America— thought that the Backward Party would be better, a finer ideal.

"We tried," the chairman went on, "both the name Forward Party and the name Backward Party, and, as you recall, the name Backwards-and-Forwards Party. We wanted something that would mean progressive and yet mean conservative . . . but we couldn't get it . . . We left, as you will remember, a committee sitting on it and they sat, at the Piccadilly, all that night but failed to find it. I'm glad to say that there has since come in the brilliant suggestion of a member—I won't name him—but you all know him, who gives us the title *The Non-Party Party* . . ."

Great applause . . . and cries . . . "Carried! Carried!"

Hoggitt explained to me on the side that the name came from Prof. Woodstick, Professor of Greek, who's in the party. In fact some of them call him the "brains of the party." Hoggitt thinks they'll probably have to drop him. People don't like the idea of brains running a party. Look at Washington or at Ottawa—at the successful parties. Still I'll say in favor of Professor Woodstick, he doesn't *look* educated . . .

The chairman came and sat with us, while a man—I didn't catch his name—was talking on what shall we do to get the farmer's vote. It seems he's a member of the platform committee (subsection farming), but Mr. Mills the chairman says they'll probably have to shift him off. He looks too countrified. Anyway nobody listened much. He was talking mostly about his own little place out near Knowlton—no, I've got that wrong—out past Knowlton; he said he wouldn't call it exactly a farm, but we could call it a farm if we liked, so I called it a farm. It appears he grows a lot of stuff on it, more lettuce, for instance, than his wife can eat, in fact, nearly enough for the horse . . . Well, you know what farm talk is at political meetings; he asked how many had seen the new type of dry silo? They hadn't . . .

But what he got to at length was the committee platform to catch the farm interest. I saw right away it was certainly good—"to give to all farmers a proper aggregate share of their own produce." That's the very thing to attract farmers. Someone wanted to insert the word "just" make it read a "just share." But it was explained that the Liberals gave them that. They've had that since 1896.

There was a lot of unanimity and good feeling over that but on the other hand a lot of difficulty over the question of labor. The man who got up to talk (I didn't catch his name, something like Fitkin, or Delbosse—a name like that)—anyway, he said he was a lawyer and couldn't pretend to speak of labor but he said he had the deepest sympathy for labor but all the same it was hard even for a lawyer to get a formula to satisfy labor. A lot of the labor men now, he explained, are mighty well educated and it's hard to put anything past them; difficult to find words for a platform that they wouldn't see through. He'd made, he said, a conscientious attempt at some honest direct statement but everything seemed to have the same fault of giving away its meaning. He had had with him on the committee, he said, the Reverend Canon Sip . . .

There was applause at that, because everybody knows the Canon, and he was sitting right there anyway. Hoggitt explained that they had tried to keep him away but they failed; Hoggitt says it's all right to talk of popularity but the Canon makes a bad impression—too damn simple and friendly, Hoggitt said. "It won't go over with the plain people . . ."

Well, he'd had with him, the lawyer said, Canon Sip and their friend Mr. Vault who as they all knew was a bank manager, or rather an ex-bank manager, whom we were all glad to see back again with us, but with all that the three of them could do, it was hard to find any adequate words that wouldn't right away show what was meant. It was no use, he said, to advocate a "just reward" for labor. That might be all right for farmers, probably too much, but labor would see through it right away. But he was glad to say that Canon Sip had suggested a labor platform that he believed would carry the country. "We propose to give to labor everywhere an entire freedom from work."

There was a lot of applause, and I must say I realized the party had hit it this time—here you had all the old slogans, "freedom to work" and "freedom of work" subsumed—that was the word the speaker used—into one lucid thought.

It was a great hit for the Canon—no wonder he's popular. You see he's not a bit like what you'd expect from a religious man—he's always cheerful, takes a drink any time, in fact he was quite tight at Peggy Sherar's wedding the other day—smokes a cigar, indeed as someone said at the meeting, he just seems the ideal of an early Christian, you know, the kind they used to burn at Rome. All the same, some of them are a little afraid of it. They say if people get the idea that a party stands for religion, it's all over with it. So Mills and Hoggitt both talk of easing Canon Sip out of the party. They would, except that having him may help to bring in the liquor interest. It seems you can't possibly hope to get anything out of the liquor interest unless you have with you some sort of showing of clergymen and professors. Lawyers don't help much for that.

Mentioning that reminds me of the main thing of the evening, the really crucial stuff, when they all sat and listened—the discussion of ways and means, how to get money to carry on.

The chairman of the interim finance committee read a report which he prefaced with a repetition of last week's general resolution in favor of fair and open means of raising funds, without secrecy or subservience to moneyed interest. He said the committee had been at work. But he said, gentlemen, before you can get to fair and open means you've got to do a good lot of spade work underground in the dark. The committee, he said, had been hard at this. The time, he said, was not ripe to say what they had been doing. But they had not been idle. They had approached already three of our largest banks for financial support, with gratifying results. The first had invited them to come back in a month; the second, to come back in three months; the third had invited

them never to come back. This, on the whole, was gratifying. They had got in touch with several manufacturing
interests; one of the members of this committee knew personally very well the head of one of these interests—or rather,
knew a lot about him—and had already obtained in this way
his pledge to give as much as he has to.

They had done their best in the direction of both the
liquor interests and the churches. But as members present
would realize, it is very hard to attract the interest of these
unless you get them together. They go, as we all know, hand
in hand. Any large, really large, contribution from a liquor
source will bring the clergy round us at once.

Meanwhile any members who would care before they
passed out to leave a small party donation would find Mr.
Sibley the treasurer at the table here. He added that Mr.
Sibley had ink and a blank cheque book. But it was too bad.
A lot of them were moving out already and I don't think they
heard about Mr. Sibley having the cheque book.

I was driven home after the meeting by one of the younger
members who had a car—a college boy, keen as anything on
politics, enthusiastic and, I could see by his talk, straight as a
string. He said he thought there were too many older men in
the thing; he was trying to engineer an inside group of young
men to get them out. That was queer, wasn't it? Because
Hoggitt had told me they'd have to get rid of a lot of the
younger men . . .

Anyway, there's no doubt what the party means.

X

THE LIFE OF LEA AND PERRINS

("There is no greater stimulus to our National Spirit than the contemplation of the lives of the great men who have made our country what it is . . .")

THE coming together of Lea and Perrins, about a century and a half ago, which was later on to have such momentous consequences, seems to have been entirely fortuitous. They met first as schoolboys at the old Winchester school. Harry Perrins, a vigorous young fellow in the Senior Fourth, came upon young Charles Lea, a new boy, standing alone in a corner of the Quad. He felt drawn to this shy, unknown lad. "What are you doing?" he asked. "Just dreaming," answered Charles. "I say," said Harry, "dreaming? That's a queer idea —dreaming of what?"

"Of a sauce," answered Charles.

"What sort of sauce?" asked Harry.

"Ah, that I don't know as yet," replied the little fellow.

That began the friendship of the two boys henceforth inseparable . . .

The boys went early to Oxford, to Worcester College, their parents being anxious to get them through it before the French Revolution broke out.

It was at Oxford that Harry Perrins learned glass blowing. "If you're still thinking of that sauce," he said to Charles Lea, "I think I could make a jolly good bottle for it."

Charles looked dreamily at his friend, "The vinegar," he said: "I'm studying chemistry."

It was on a bright morning after the Declaration of Independence that Charles Lea came early across the Quad to wake up Harry. "I can make it," he said.

A few days later in a cellar of the old Mitre Tavern Charles and Harry stood looking into a broad vat full of dark liquid. Charles threw into it a last spoonful of powder. "That's got it," he said.

"What was in that powder, Charlie?" asked Harry.

"Hush, hush," Charles said, "there are people above."

"Whisper it," said Harry.

"No, no," answered Charles, "not now."

"What do we do next?" asked Harry presently.

"We have to wait twenty-five years," said Charlie. "You can't hurry vinegar. Everybody knows that."

"What do we do in the twenty-five years?"

"We have to think out a label," said Charles. "We'll need all the time."

The twenty-five years, thus busily occupied, seemed to pass like a drop in a vat. One year Charles got the idea of a bird on the label, and within a few years more Harry seized the notion of the picture of a rabbit. A few hurried years were devoted to selecting the color, and—it seemed in no time—the thing was done.

They were ready to bottle up, still both under sixty, hale and hearty, having never touched sauce in their lives.

Then came an unforeseen delay.

"Charles," said Harry, "how do we *sell* it?"

"What do you mean?" asked Charles, still as impractical as ever.

"Sell it, sell it. Put it on the market and push it."

"It's a good sauce," protested Charles.

"Good? Of course it is—but that won't advertise it. Didn't you learn anything from the French Revolution?"

Charles was impractical, but he had a rapid mind.

"That's it," he said; "you've said it."

"What do you mean?" asked Harry.

"The French Revolution. Aristocracy? Don't you see, we'll say the sauce was made from a recipe given us by a nobleman . . ."

"Hold on," said Harry, puzzled, "a nobleman couldn't make up a recipe."

"Of course not," said Charles. "Don't you see, we'll *say* he did."

A few days later Harry turned up at Charles's rooms with a tall aristocratic man, stamped with all the stamps that mark nobility.

"This is Lord Nit of Worcester," he said. "Show him where to sign."

"You don't need to," said Harry, "just write, 'from the recipe of a nobleman of that county'."

Lord Nit took the pen.

"I say," he said, "rather good that, eh?"

With that the sauce was on.

The busy years spun past, expanding the British Empire as the need for the sauce kept bulging it outwards.

There was still much to do. Eager years passed in the quest of a glass stopper and a cork, involving the expulsion of the Portuguese Royal Family.

Charles and Harry, still hale and hearty, confidently expected to live on into the reign of Queen Victoria.

But it was not to be.

There came a day when a breathless manservant broke into Harry's study . . .

"Could you come over, sir, at once?" he managed to say. "It's Mr. Charles. He's real bad."

"What's he been taking?" asked Harry.

"Some of the sauce, I'm afraid, sir."

"Good Lord!" gasped Harry.

Harry leant over Charles's bed. It seemed as if they were back again, boys together, in the old Winchester Quad, with Charlie still dreaming.

"Charlie," murmured Harry, "Charlie, can you still hear me? What was in the spoon?"

But there came no answer.

XI

A MORNING OFF

("It is the duty of each and every one of us to maintain in war-time not only an unflinching courage but even a cheerful optimism that defies misfortune."—Winston Churchill, Mrs. Roosevelt, and other speakers.)

I READ that motto, hanging on my wall just before starting out this morning. But for once I didn't need it, because I'm in for a cheery morning anyway.

I'm going down to my dentist, and what do you think? He said he could give me the whole morning if need be! Think of that, eh?

So here I sit snug and cosy in the big chair, the great plate glass window in front of me, the sun pouring in and the birds singing outside. My dentist friend walks round in his white coat—now I see him, now I don't see him. You see I have my head in a V-shaped affair—for Victory. I never thought of it before!—and so I can't move it sideways. He needs my head that way when we're using the large augur, the two-inch, going at high speed.

For the moment my dental friend is out of the room, telephoning, I imagine. The merry fellow is so popular with all his friends that they seem to ring him up every few minutes.

Little scraps of his conversation reach my ears as I lie half-buried in my white towel, in a sweet reverie of expectancy . . .

"Pretty bad in the night, was it, eh? Well, perhaps you'd

better come along down and we'll make a boring through that biscuspid and see what's there!"

Full of ideas, he is, always like that—never discouraged, something new to suggest all the time. And then I hear him say; "Well, let me see. I'm busy now for about a couple of hours"—hurrah! That means me! I was so afraid he was going to say "I'll be through here in about five minutes." But no, it's all right; I've got two long, dreamy hours in front of me.

He comes back into the room and his cheery presence, as he searches among his instruments and gives a preliminary buzz to the buzzer, seems to make the sunshine even brighter. How pleasant life seems—the dear old life; that is, the life I quitted ten minutes ago and to which, please Providence, I hope to return in two hours. I never felt, till I sat here, how full and pleasant life is.

So runs my pleasant reverie. But, meanwhile, my dental friend has taken up a little hammer and has tapped me in his playful way, on the back teeth.

"Feel that?" he says.

And he's right, the merry dog! I do feel it. He guessed it right away. I am hoping so much that he will hit me again.

Come on, let's have a little more fun like that. But no. He's laid aside his hammer and as nearly as we can see has rolled up his cuffs to the elbow and has started his good old electric buzzer into a roar.

Ah, ha! Now we are going to get something—this is going to be the big fun, the real thing. That's the greatest thing about our little dental mornings, there's always something new. Always as I sit I have a pleasant expectancy that my dental friend is planning a new one.

Now, then, let us sit back tight, while he drives at our jaw with the buzzer. Of all the exhilarating feelings of hand-to-hand conflict of man against man, of mind matched against mind, and intelligence pitted against intelligence, I know of none more stimulating than when we brace ourselves for this conflict of man and machinery.

He has on his side the power of electricity and the force of machinery. But I am not without resource. I brace myself, laughingly, in my chair while he starts to bore. We need, in fact, our full strength; but, on the other hand, if he tries to keep up at this pace his hands will get tired. I realize, with a sense of amusement, that if his machine slips, he may get a nasty thump on the hand against my jawbone.

A female voice speaking into the room has called him to the telephone, and again I am alone. What if he never comes back!

The awful thought leaps to my mind, what if he comes in and says, "I'm sorry to say I have to take a train out of town at once." How terrible!

Perhaps he'll come in and say, "Excuse me, I have to leave instantly for Ungava!" or, "I'll have to let your work go; they've sent for me to go to China!"

But no, how lucky! Back he comes again. I've not lost him. And now what is he at? Stuffing cotton-wool up into my head, wool saturated with some kind of drugs, and pounding it in with a little hammer.

And then—all of a sudden, so it seems—he steps back and says, "There, that will do nicely till Monday."

Never mind! After all, he said Monday! It won't seem so long till then!

XII

MR. PLUMTER, B.A., REVISITS THE OLD SHOP

(Remember now thy college in the days of thy graduation.—Ecclesiastes—Improved).

MR. ARCHIE PLUMTER, college graduate, lives in one of those towns that lie fast asleep in the garden part of Western Ontario. You know the little places—all trees and grass and hedges and flowers, with the houses well back from the street and all boulevarded together. In Woodsdale you can't tell where the McLeans' lawn ends and Dr. Selby's begins. Somewhere concealed in the middle of the town is the main street with the shops on it, and away off at the side, down hill, is the railway station, which is really more of a lawn and a flower garden than a station. All the big through trains stop at Woodsdale (for water) and the passengers ask the porter what place this is and he looks out of the window and shakes his head.

But it's just the place for a college graduate. You see, a college graduate, as Plumter himself says, could hardly stand it in the country. His mind is too active. But here—again as Archie himself explains—you have everything, just as in the city. If you want to do any shopping you get anything you want right here on the main street; say you want a pair of boots—they have them; say you want a necktie, they'll have it, or they'll send for it. And, anyway, if you have any big shopping, any serious buying to do, you've only to hop on the train and even the slow train runs you into the City in three hours, and the flyer does it in two and three quarters. There's a picture house in town or if you want to go to the theatres you've only to step on the train and there you are, in Detroit. How long? About four hours. Or if you want music, well, what's the matter with taking a steamer across Lake Erie to Cleveland? That's what Archie Plumter does, or at least that's not what he does but it's what he could do if he did it. Or suppose you want a drink? Well, you can't get a drink in Woodsdale because it's local option and so they have no choice. But all you have to do is jump in the car, drive twelve miles and get all you want.

Mr. Plumter is in the milling business (flour and feed). 'That's his mill—as it was his father's—that huge stone grist mill, sunk down so deep in Woodsdale Creek that, big as it is, the trees have overgrown and overtopped it. A stone grist mill is one of the few of man's contrivances which, with a touch of time's hand, can even improve on nature. There it stands, with the water pounding over the dam beside it, and churning up white foam among the stones below; a roar of water outside, and inside a never ending trembling and vibration of the floors, as the great mill stones hum as drowsily and steadily as the earth upon its axis . . . The floors all a-tremble, and on them the millers, moving bags of flour on little hand trucks and talking with the incoming farmers with one hand to their ear. After work the millers go home, dusted all over with fine white—looking better men—right out of the Bible.

Thus roars and thunders Plumter's mill and it seems now

that it is to start to grind grist for Mr. Plumter's old college. . . .

It has been my fortune at intervals to pass through Woodsdale on the through trains, and I often stop over between the flyer and the slow train, or contrariwise, and spend a few hours with Archie Plumter. He and I were at college together twenty years or more ago and so when we meet Archie's talk is all college—all about the "old shop" as he loves to call it. How is it getting on? Have I been round it at all lately?

Oddly enough, in the twenty years since our graduation Archie has never once been "back:" and this, despite the fact that he's in and out of the city, as he himself says, practically all the time, certainly every two years or so. He means to go to the college! . . . always *means* to . . . every time he takes a trip to the city he tells Nell (that's his wife) that he means to have a look around the old joint. But he never does. You see he always has some business in the morning, and generally he takes "some feller" out to lunch, and is apt to meet "one or two fellers" on the street—when a man as genial and comfortable as Archie Plumter comes to the city, the whole street seems filled with accidental "good fellers" as genial as himself.

So he doesn't go. That's nothing. Most graduates are like that, even right in the city. They never go near the old college, unless it's in a bee line between their house and their office. Often they don't see it for ten years. That's nothing to do with their enthusiasm.

Plumter is keen on college. He tells me that they often talk, Dr. Selby and himself, of getting up a college dinner right there in Woodsdale. It seems they've quite a group of graduates. As Archie says, counting himself and Dr. Selby—and Dr. Selby and himself—and not counting the Methodist minister because you would hardly expect him to take anything, there'd be ten of the boys altogether, or eleven if you count the druggist. They often talk of a dinner. But there are difficulties. At a college dinner the boys would naturally like to wear dinner jackets. But there are two of the boys who haven't got dinner jackets. So that has held the thing up—just as it has for many college dinners from Halifax to Pasadena.

So I wasn't surprised when about a couple of weeks ago I got a letter from Archie which said, "If you are coming through here soon I'd be glad if you'd stay over and have dinner some evening. I have some college stuff to ask you about —important stuff—but I'd rather talk about it than explain it in a letter."

Naturally I took occasion as soon as I could stay from afternoon local to the night flyer.

It was one of those beautiful evenings in late September, everything soft and still and mellow; the water in the dam was lower and the water below the dam was quieter, and the main street drowsier and the trees heavier—and the gladioli and asters and late petunias and golden glow banked round the houses and all of Woodsdale hazy and soft with that touch of Indian summer that would have touched even an Indian.

Archie Plumter's house—but you know exactly what that would be like—large and low—sandstone and red brick, and half timber, with sweeping porches and verandahs and clipped grass and flowers, yet as if all in a woodland.

"There's the old college," Archie said as he led me into the library and pointed to a picture. "Nell will be down in a minute. Pretty good of the old joint, isn't it? Just take a good look at it while I shake up a cocktail."

The reader must make no mistake about that cocktail. I said above that you can't get drinks in Woodsdale. Neither can you. This was just some rye and vermouth that Archie had in the house. In fact that's the only way they can get it —to have it in the house.

"I've got some stuff to talk about," said Archie, "but I'd sooner let it keep till after dinner . . ."

We drank the cocktail and in came Nell. Archie Plumter has been as comfortable and fortunate in his marriage as in everything else. Nell's father was a lumberman; in fact, he was a big lumberman, one of the biggest, and there's something about that business of the forest almost as warm and natural as flour and feed, or big scale farming. Poets may talk as they like about a fisherman's daughter who lives on the water. But for matrimony, for comfortable companionship and financial strength, give me a lumberman's daughter every time. "Nell, you remember," said Archie as we shook hands, "was at college too. But she, of course, didn't go on to a degree."

No, of course she didn't. Anyone as pretty as she must have been twenty years ago didn't need a degree. She could pick up something easier at college than that.

"Nell," said Archie, "was a partial."

Was she really? You'd hardly think so now. She looks pretty complete. Still, the years have used her kindly.

"I was just showing this picture of the old circus," continued Archie. "That picture was taken the first year I played on the football team. You remember, Nell, the big game when the college moved up to second place but I couldn't play because of my wrist?"

No doubt Nell remembered it all right: but more likely as the game when he held her hand under the rug on the football benches, and she realized that perhaps she wouldn't need to go any further with mathematics. College girls have their own calendar. They don't remember the day the college gave an honorary degree to the British Ambassador. They remember the day they first wore their dark blue dress with the fur collar.

We went into dinner, one of those excellent and solid dinners, heavy with steak and light with claret and fragrant with coffee and cigars—the kind of real dinner only to be arranged by a lumberman's daughter who remembers feeding her father—just the thing to nourish the trained college brain. The claret, fortunately, was some that Archie had in the cellar; so was the Scotch whiskey that we had afterwards —just stuff out of the cellar.

All through dinner Archie was full of reminiscences and questions and filled with by-gone admiration.

"What became of Professor Crabbe, the Greek Professor?"

"He's still there, I think," I said.

"Some of the fellows didn't like him so much," said Archie, "and of course I never took Greek. But he was certainly a wizard. That man had the most remarkable and the most ready memory I ever came across. I asked him one day, for instance, what was the date of the foundation of Babylon."

"And did he answer?"

"Answered right off—not a moment's hesitation—said he didn't recall it. He certainly was a wonder."

Indeed from our dinner talk that evening the college in Plumter's days had been instructed by a set of "wizards," "wonders" and "wows," an illumination that never comes twice to a college.

"What became of old Professor Dim, the historian?" Archie asked.

"He's still right there," I said, "as far as I know. I haven't been actually inside the college for about a year but I'm sure he's there . . . Pretty old, of course."

"He must be. Do you remember the day I knocked him down in the corridor and the old fellow was nice about it? You remember the way we used to come rushing out of the First Year Latin lecture at twelve o'clock, all in a stampede, and I knocked the old fellow down and Bill, the janitor, picked him up. Where's Bill? When did he die?"

"He's not dead," I said, "he's there." Archie Plumter, like all stay-away graduates, imagined everybody had died since he went away.

After dinner Nell went upstairs to help their two little girls with their algebra. That's where Nell's education as a partial comes in, eh?—able to help the little girls (theyr'e twelve and fourteen) with their algebra. That is, help them as far as simultaneous equations. They'll have to stop there. But they won't need quadratics—pretty little girls like those.

Archie unfolded his ideas over the Scotch and cigars. "What I feel is," he said, "I've been a pretty poor sort of graduate. What have I ever done for the old joint, except a casual subscription and things of that sort? Well—I've been doing pretty well lately—I want to give the college some money. I want to give it twenty-five thousand dollars. Now, here's the point. How do I go about it? What do I do? Where do I get the excuse?"

"Excuse?" I said.

"Yes. How do I start it?"

"Archie," I said, "you don't need any excuse when you give a college money. They'll find the excuse: you just find the money. What do you want to do, endow a set of lectures, or offer a fellowship—or just ask them what to do?"

"Oh, I know just what I want to give," Plumter said. "I want to give a clock—a clock set in a little tower so that students in the campus can see the time. Do you know, when I went to college I had no watch—at least I had an old silver watch of father's, but it wouldn't go."

"I know," I said, "all students used to have old silver watches that wouldn't go. Now they have new gunmetal watches that will."

"Well, this clock I want to give," said Archie, "does more than tell the time. I got the idea from one that Nell and I saw on our trip this summer to California, at one of those old missions. It has chimes inside it, and just before it strikes the hour it strikes a chime.

Bing! Bong! Bong!
Bong! Bing! Bing!

"The most melodious thing I ever heard," Archie said.

It seemed to me that I had heard things more melodious than Plumter's rendering of a chime. But his own opinion was different. He repeated his chimes.

Bing! Bong! Bong!
Bong! Bing! Bing!

And he added: "I've got all the data on the whole thing in a business way. It would cost twenty-five thousand and the contractor could hook the clock tower on at any spot on the roof they like. So, what do I do next?"

"Why," I said, "go down to the city and go and see the president and tell him about it. That's all. That will give you a look round the place."

"That's so," he assented, "that's right. I'll have a look at the old shop. I'll come next week. You must meet me at the train."

So a week after that Plumter came up from Woodsdale to the city to make his benefaction.

I met him at the station. It was only half-past eight on a bright autumn morning, but he was nervous already. He began at once. "What I think I'll say, I'll say, 'Mr. President, I'm afraid I've been rather a delinquent graduate, but . . .' Something like that, eh?"

I said that would be fine. At breakfast, and after, he was still rehearsing it; " 'Mr. President, I'm afraid . . .' I won't beat about the bush," he said. "I'll go right at it, eh?"

He had no notion how easy it is to give twenty-five thousand dollars to a college. You don't have to find the words; just the money.

So in the middle morning we started for the college. I hadn't realized till we came to the gates of the campus how much it has changed since Plumter had left it twenty years ago—the beautiful big Mines Building, all white stone, on one side of the campus and the new library, of white stone and slots of glass on the other.

Plumter stopped dead as we entered the campus.

"I'll be damned!" he said as he looked round it. "Is this

all the size it was? No bigger than this? I thought it was twice the size."

Then he said, "What's that?"

"That's the new Mines building," I said.

"Where's the old one, the little old red brick building?"

"They knocked it down," I explained.

"Knocked it down!" repeated Plumter. "Good Lord, knocked it down! And what's the other building?"

"That's the new library," I said; "the old one was knocked down ten years ago."

"You mean they knocked down the library?" said Plumter. He sounded horrified. Then with evident relief, he exclaimed, "Say, there's the old museum, yes, sir, the same darned old museum! I'm certainly glad to see it again."

"You used to be in it much?" I asked.

"I never was in it," said Plumter. "There was ten cents admission, you remember?"

All this time little flocks of students, boys and girls, were overtaking and passing us, for this was the crowded time of the morning with the big lectures of the first and second year going on.

"Who are all these?" asked Plumter. "Is there partly a high school here now?"

"No," I said, "these are the students."

"Good Lord!" said Plumter and stood still to let a demure little group of seventeen-year-old girls go past. One of the demure little girls was saying as she went by, "I don't care what you call it, I call it a hell of a poor course . . ."

And just at that moment we ran into Professor Crabbe. Plumter hailed him with outstretched hand.

"How do you do, sir . . . you remember me . . . I hope . . . I'm Plumter."

"Oh, perfectly well, perfectly well," said the professor, "perfectly well."

They shook hands.

"And what are you in now, Mr. Platter?" asked Professor Crabbe.

"I'm in the milling industry, sir," said Plumter.

"In the ministry!" said Professor Crabbe. "Dear me . . . well, you were always heading that way, heading that way! Your Greek must come very well for your sermons.

"I never took any," said Plumter.

"Of course," said the Professor.

"You're still lecturing, sir?" asked Plumter.

"All except my eyesight," answered Professor Crabbe. "My hearing is excellent, Mr. Plaster"—and he gave him a challenging look.

"You can still see for bookwriting, sir," said Plumter pleasantly.

"I never see him," said the professor. "In your class, wasn't he? But I never see him now, haven't for years. Time moves on, you know—well, good-bye, Mr. Blister."

But there was more cheer and consolation in meeting Bill, the janitor, as we went into Arts Building, Bill who was timeless and ageless, and remembered everything.

"Well, Mr. Plumter, where you been all this time? We thought you was never coming back!"

"You remember me, eh?" said Plumter, much gratified.

"Remember you?" laughed Bill, "I should say so! You was a regular holy terror! More breakages to your name, Mr. Plumter, than any other student in college!"

Plumter joined in the laugh. He must tell them in Woodsdale about that "holy terror" stuff.

Just then there burst into the main hall through the opening class room door the full charge and onslaught of "Latin One Men" coming out after the lecture. It was like what we used to read of the stampede of Texas steers . . . Plumter was swept aside, pounded and jostled in the flooding pushing crowd; but all so polite, those boys. "Sorry, sir," they'd say as they ran into his stomach. "Excuse me, sir," as they got him in the small of his back . . .

"What's all this?" asked Plumter.

"First Year Latin coming out, sir . . . but Lord! That's nothing to what it was in your day. Remember when you knocked down Professor Dim?"

And as the flood subsided who should be standing there but Professor Dim, Professor of History and Archaeology. There he was just as ancient and as diminutive, as rosy and as cheery as ever—just as young at seventy as he had been old at fifty. There he was, gown and all, and his lectures, all in leather, under his arm. Being a professor of history he could remember anything up to three thousand years . . .

"Why, how do you, Mr. Plumter," he said, "how do you do. This is really a pleasure . . ."

"I'm very glad to see you, sir; I always wish I'd been fortunate enough to take your lectures."

"Ah, now, that's very kind of you! I wonder if you wouldn't care perhaps to come in and sit and listen now . . . oh no, these are not the old lectures of your time—this is a new course—it's only the sixth year I've given it—a course on the Crusades . . . But do come . . . I've just a small class . . . a dozen . . . I often have visitors drop in . . . only last month a young Chinaman came in . . . accidentally . . . but he was delighted . . . Please do."

So genial, so anxious, old Professor Dim, with that queer conceit a professor never loses—so what could we say?

"That's right," said Professor Dim. "William here will show you the room."

The class were already there, seated and decorously waiting—a professor's "dozen" of them, that is, seven. Anyone acquainted with a college register could have explained just who they were and why they were there: three divinity students who were taking the Crusades as a credit in Christianity, a football student taking it as a football qualification, a history student who was liable to the Crusades because he'd fallen down on the French Revolution, and two women Sociology students who had been compelled by a clash in the time-table to substitute the Crusades in place of a course in Motherhood which came at the wrong hour.

From the side door in came Professor Dim. He took his place behind his reading desk, unfolded and spread the blue fool's-cap sheets of the Crusades, bowed courteously to the class, and began:—

"Heliogabalus—" began Professor Dim.

"I beg your pardon, sir," said the football man.

"Heliogabalus, Mr. Munro—" repeated Professor Dim.

"Thank you, sir—"

"Heliogabalus," said Professor Dim, for the third time—and paused while all the class wrote down Heliogabalus . . .

"having now assumed the purple . . ." announced Professor Dim.

"purple" . . . wrote the class.

A college lecture is a queer thing, for people not accustomed to it. The Professor isn't exactly dictating the lecture, and he isn't exactly talking, and the class are not exactly taking dictation and they're not exactly listening. It's a system they both have grown so used to that it's second nature.

But for anyone to have to sit and listen to it, without writing down anything, not even "purple," is, of course, impossible. It's excruciating. I could watch Archie Plumter suffering; trying to look interested; trying to listen; trying to not listen. I knew just what he was thinking; he was wondering if it was really true that he had had four years of this! That he had gone not to one lecture in a morning but to two, three or even four of them!

So he sat agonizing. Then I found in my pocket a pencil and I took some sheets of paper "off" a divinity student behind us, and gave them to Plumter. Oh, my! what a change! What a transformation!

He happened to get the chance of a real start . . . Professor Dim had just opened up. "In the year A.D. 940, or, if you prefer it, the Arabian year 318 . . ." Oh, my! that was stuff! Mr. Plumter's pencil flew over the paper . . . In five minutes he was absorbed—in ten minutes lost to the world, in the fascination, the concentration of taking notes. Old habit and forgotten aptitude sprang again to life. He wrote and spelt such names Godroi de Bouillon and Saladin Ben Shirgah as easily as you jump a ditch in a van! Think what it would mean, how wonderful it would be, to spend four years like this, with perhaps two or three lectures every morning!!

After the lecture we shook hands with Professor Dim—the Professor a little flushed, a little flurried but as happy over praise as a schoolboy.

"Certainly a wonderful lecture, sir," said Plumter, his notes all collected into a precious heap.

"I'm so glad you liked it," said Professor Dim. "It's one of four—as I say, a special course—when I get it into shape, in a year or two, my hope is to open the course to the public . . . if I had a large hall . . ."

"You'd certainly draw a big crowd," said Archie Plumter, and he meant it.

And then to see the President. Down the corridor and along and through and up, and so to the President's outer office, where we sent in Plumter's card and waited.

Archie, I saw, was all nervous again. I could hear him reciting.

The President's lady secretary, filing cards, said it was a fine day, and Plumter didn't hear her.

She filed some more and then asked him where he lived, and, he remembered and said, "Woodsdale." Then the buzzer buzzed and she said that the President would see us now, and so in we went.

The President rose and shook hands—with me, casually, as to someone known, but with Plumter, as evidently the main visitor, the person of the occasion.

"How do you do?" he said, "Mr.—" as he looked down at the little card—"Mr. Plumter, is it not?"

"Yes," Plumter said.

"Ah, yes," said the President, "Mr. Plumter of the class of . . . class of . . ."

"Yes," Plumter said.

"And you're now living in—"

"Woodsdale," Plumter said.

At that moment the lady secretary slipped into the room, said something into the President's ear to which he answered in a low voice, "Ask him kindly to wait—about five minutes."

"Woodsdale!" he said. "Woodsdale, oh, yes, that's out— out beyond . . ."

"Yes," said Plumter.

"And what profession are you following, Mr. Plumter?" asks the President.

"I'm not in a profession," Archie said. "I'm mostly in feed."

The President hadn't the least idea what he meant; it certainly sounded pretty hoggish but he answered as pleasantly as he could, "Ah, yes, you're in feed, eh!"

Just then the desk telephone on the table made a gurgling sound; the President picked it up, listened, and said, "Oh, yes, very pleased, indeed, yes, in about five minutes."

The brief pause had enabled Plumter to collect his courage for the effort he had to make. He determined to say what he had to and be done with it.

He rose and stood up—it seemed more formal and natural to say it in that attitude.

"Mr. President," he said, "I'm afraid I—" and he cleared his throat.

The President had risen also and put out his hand with a smile; he thought Plumter was leaving . . . He would have liked to speak of lunch, but with a man mostly in feed it seemed risky.

But just as he began to speak there fell upon our ears, from somewhere outside, the loud and melodious sound of a chime of bells:

Bing! Bong! Bong!
Bong! Bing! Bing!

"Ah"—said the President, his head on one side and an appreciative smile on his face— "Ah! Our new chimes! Beautiful, aren't they? The gift of one of our graduates, a clock tower with a chime! You may have noticed it on the left as you came up!"

As we walked away from the building I said, "I'm sorry, Archie, I didn't know about those chimes; I haven't been round here for a year; they are evidently just new."

"Oh, that's all right," he said, and he added, "To hell with them!"

And just then a little incident happened to cheer him up. For there was good old Bill, the janitor, running down the front steps . . . "Just to say good-bye, if you're off, sir," he called, and as he joined us, "Hope you'll come again before long, sir."

"Thanks very much Bill . . ."

"And here's a little note, sir, that I was to give you. The Bursar heard you was round, sir, and he said not to let you go without this. It's a bill for breakages he's had, sir, for years and years. He'd lost your address."

As we moved off down the avenue, we saw in the sideways distance Professor Dim starting off for home, his Crusades, all in leather, under his arm—he waved his hand in good-bye. "That old bird," said Plumter, "is worth the whole dam lot of them."

Depressed? You'd be surprised how fast that sort of thing wears off . . . By the time we'd had a cocktail at the club, Plumter was beginning to feel as if we'd had a pretty notable morning . . . By the time we'd had lunch, he was explaining to men at the club that he'd been having a look round the old shop . . . and that the new Mines Building was certainly all right . . .

For you see, after all, he hadn't bought the clock, he still had his twenty-five thousand dollars, and already a new idea was dawning on his mind . . . By the time he got to Woodsdale he was full of it all, more of a graduate than ever.

The Woodsdale *By-path* (Archie owned it) . . . printed in the next issue some interesting *Notes on the Third Crusade,* beginning "Heliogabalus, having assumed the purple . . ."

And a few weeks after that the "college boys" of Woodsdale pulled off their college dinner—put on their dinner jackets and pulled the dinner off. One of the two had bought one and the other one borrowed one—so it was all right. Archie Plumter made the speech of the evening, and he said that a college graduate who didn't from time to time, say at least once in twenty years, visit the old place was as low as a snake.

But just a litttle after that came the big thing, the announcement in all the city papers, of the foundation of an endowment at the college of a series of Four Lectures on the Crusades, to be given annually by the greatest scholars in the world. You'll see the lectures listed now right there in the front pages of the calendar among Endowments and Benefactions. They're called *The Dim Lectures on the Crusades, endowed by Archibald and Helen Plumter*—four of them endowed at five hundred dollars each. Professor Dim will give them the first ten years and after that they'll be thrown open to all the scholars of the world. My! Won't there be a scramble?

XIII

ALLEGORY ISLAND

FOUR business men were stranded, shipwrecked and penniless, upon an island in the South Seas. It was a beautiful island. Breadfruit grew on every tree, coconuts dangled at the tops of palms, while beds of oysters lay near the shore.

But for the business men it was useless. They had no "funds" to develop the island; with an advance of funds they could have gathered breadfruit and made bread. But without funds! Why, they couldn't They must stay hungry.

"Don't you think," said the weakest among them—a frail man (he had never been able to raise more than a million dollars; he'd no strength)—"Don't you think," he said to the biggest man, "you could climb that palm tree and throw down coconuts?" . . . "And who'll underwrite me?" asked the other.

There it was! They were blocked and helpless; couldn't even get an advance to wade into the sea for oysters.

So they sat there on the rocks—starving, dejected, their hair growing long. They couldn't even shave; there was no barbers union.

On the fourth day the frail man, who was obviously sinking, said:

"If I die I want you to bury me over there on that little hill overlooking the sea."

"We can't bury you, Eddie," they said. "We've no burial fund."

They fell asleep on the sands. But the next morning when they woke up an Angel was standing beside them. They knew he was an Angel although he wore a morning coat and a top hat, and had grey striped trousers with spats above his boots.

"Are you an Angel?" they asked.

"Pretty much," he answered. "That is to say, I am a director of the Bank of England, but for you just now it's almost the same thing."

"Funds, funds!" they exclaimed. "Can you advance us funds?"

"Certainly," said the Angel. "I came for that. I think I see a fountain pen in your waistcoat pocket there. Thank you . . . and that ten cent scribbler . . . much obliged. Now then up you get! Light a fire, go and collect those oysters, pick some breadfruit, chase that wild goat and I'll arrange an advance of funds while you're doing it."

As they sat round their fire at supper the Angel explained it all out of the scribbler.

"I have capitalized your island at two million dollars (that's half a million each) and I have opened a current drawing account for each of you of a hundred thousand, with loans as required . . ."

What activity next day! Climb the coconut tree? Why, of course, the man was underwritten. Oysters? They wrote out an oyster policy and waded right in up to their necks.

What a change the next week or so brought! There they sat at lunch in their comfortable Banyan Club House overlooking the sea—(annual dues, a thousand dollars a year)—sat at lunch eating grilled oysters with coconut cocktails . . .

"To think," said the little man Eddie, "that only a week ago I wanted to die!"

"All right now, anytime, Eddie," said another . . . "We've a mutual burial and benefit fund. Ask the Angel if we haven't."

But when they looked round the Angel had vanished.

"Too bad," said the senior man. "But in a way it doesn't matter so much now. We can hire a clergyman. I propose we pay big money and get a really good one."

It's almost a pity to mention the sequel. A little later, four laboring men tried to land on the island. The others undertook to fight them off with shotguns. That started civilization. But the pity was that if they had only had the Angel with them, he would have told them to let the laborers land and to multiply all the figures in the book by two, and add a little extra, because in developing a country blessed by ample resources twice four is ten.

But the coming of labour was really only part of what happened. Just as the trouble with capital began a boatload of women was blown ashore, and then two separate canoes with rival missionaries. So that started a still more complete civilization, with machinery and increase of population till presently there were enough of them on the island to pick up sides for a war, then for a bigger war, and at last an extermination.

So, after they were all exterminated there lay Allegory Island again, empty and beautiful in the sunshine. The wind sang and the waves whitened as they rose, or sank to mere ruffles on the surface of the ocean. Then, as the days and the years went by, the lapse of time and the luxuriance of nature wiped out all trace of the visitation of civilization, and of its angers, its wars and death. There lay Allegory Island again as nature made it.

Then, at last, after many years, there came sailing to the island a ship of Socialists. And these had come across the ocean looking for a place to set up Brotherly Love. But they had been a long time in coming, for it is much slower to sail a ship on brotherly love than in the old Nova Scotia fashion.

So when the leader saw Allegory Island it looked so fresh and green and cool that he knew it was just the place for a habitation of brotherly love. He called down the main hatch-way, "Gentlemen, I don't want to ask you to overexert your-selves and I don't want to disturb the ladies, but if some of you will come on deck I think you will agree that we have found just the very place we are looking for."

They came at once, after a while, for they were the best-natured fellows in the world.

So presently they got the ship to the shore. They bumped a hole in it on the rocks but that didn't matter as they wouldn't be using it any more. They had speeches and sang community songs and went to sleep on the sands with the wind in their ears.

The next day the leader said, "Now, gentlemen, I suggest that we set ourselves to work for the production of food. Labour, ladies and gentlemen, is the sole source of value. I will, therefore, ask you to initiate with me the production of yams, mangoes, banyans, breadfruit and so forth, and the domestication of the wild dingo and the llama for their wool and of the goat for its milk and meat. We will also search the rocks for guano eggs."

One shook his head. "It sounds like work," he said.

But the leader answered, "How can it be work if you get no wages?"

And another said, "Can't we have a little community singing first?" So they sat and sang.

After that—not that very day, of course—the work began, or at least it was supposed to begin. But the Island was so beautiful and so drowsy that it hardly seemed right to work. Even the leader said, "Don't overexert yourselves, ladies and gentlemen, and, above all, keep out of the sun. Mrs. McSpodden, don't try to catch that goat—you'll never get it."

So the yam field was a little scratched and then neglected, and they sat round on the grass in the shade of the trees and listened to the burbling of the little brooks, and the women made daisy chains of flowers and sang to the children, and it always seemed too early to begin work, and then too late, and then it was afternoon and then sunset.

So they ate what they had brought in boxes and crates and barrels, and each day there was less and less of it. "We must work," said the leader and yawned as he said it, and when they looked at him again he was fast asleep.

Then came all of a sudden the monsoon storms and rain, and great flashes of lightning that tore the sky, and wind and waves that smashed what was left of the ship. And there was no shelter and no food and only hissing rain.

And when the monsoon storm was over the Socialist settlement of Brotherly Love was gone. There was nothing of it but here and there little fragments of human wreckage among the rocks and trees, and bits of coloured cloth—and even that the sun and wind tore and wore away every day. Perhaps some of the people made a raft of the broken ship and got away. But if they did it was never known.

Years and years went by—centuries. And with the flight of time, nature wiped away—oh, so, easily—the little traces of man's brief visit. A tangled vine here, a cluster of tall flowers there and it was all gone; a little calcined whiteness that once was bone, crumbling to nothing; a piece of steel oxydizing in the air till it blew away as red dust on the wind.

So once again Allegory Island was empty and the wind sang and the waves whitened and the tide marked out on the sand the record of the passing years. So many years went by, we say, that every trace of the capitalists civilization and the Socialists dream was past and gone, blown away with the wind, and rotted into the soil.

Then there came over the waves other and distant people. For these were Polynesian savages, inured for uncounted generations to the seas and islands of the Pacific . . . In a huge open boat they came, light and buoyant, all of hide and wicker and leaping the surface of the waves . . . There was a great square sail in the boat, and far out on the lee side reached an outrigger of long poles that held a float . . . Twenty flat paddles flashed in the sun on either side, and there were in all—men, women and children—sixty-two people on board . . .

The boat had come five hundred miles over the waves—but that was nothing to it . . .

As they drew near the island the paddlers, since there

might be lurking enemies on the shore, chanted out their war-song . . .

A: Ki—a: Ki—a: Ki—a.

But there was no one there. They drove the boat high on the sand and landed in peace.

And here it would take the pen of a professor of archaeology to tell of "primitive culture" and explain how these savages were fitted to their environment, how easy it was to them to meet difficulties that had meant failure and death to civilized Europeans. Their boat, their knowledge of the sea—everything prepared and foreseen, not by foresight, but by instinct.

Even their food. There was no danger of starvation for them.

They had their food with them. We said there were sixty two on the boat, the long boat that rode so easily. Two of them were tied up in thongs under the fore-peak of the boat. They were the food; plenty for a warm meal tonight, enough cold for tomorrow and another hot roast next week.

So now you can understand better the raptures of the archaeologists over primitive culture and its adaptation . . .

So it was that the savages, after a comfortable meal, sat around their little fire, which was dying low in the dusk of the warm summer evening, the soft moon just rising out of civilization. The fireflies played about them, little dots of phosphorescence in the dark—and the women sat and crooned their soft Polynesian love songs, and patted the little children's hands as they fell asleep.

Savages love one, don't they?

So all that would be needed would be for the savages to

tay two or three thousand years on Allegory Island, and get
civilized and start the round again.

I hope there are no readers of this book who are people who want to
now things. If there are they may want to know whether there were ever
slands in the Pacific as beautiful and inviting as Allegory Island, and
whether savages could really make a voyage of five hundred miles in an open
boat. For the island, as good and indeed far better, they may see that fas-
inating old book *Anson's Voyage Around the World* (1740-44) where they
may read of the South Seas Paradise Island of Tinian (lat 15' 8" North and
ongitude close to the date line of longitude 180°), and for voyages of savages
n open boats across five hundred miles of the Pacific, and even double that
distance, they may see that fascinating new book Vilhjalmur Stefansson's
Greenland.

But why do so?

XIV

DAMON AND PYTHIAS, BARRISTERS, SOLICITORS, ETC.

You remember Damon and Pythias, of course—or at least you remember them as well as I do—the two famous friends in Roman history, or in Greek history, I forget which. The history of Syracuse, you say? Well! well! to think of that! Syracuse in New York State? Oh, the Greek Syracuse in Greece! Oh, not in Greece—the Greek Syracuse not in Greece! I'm glad to know exactly where it all was.

Anyway, as you remember, wherever Damon went Pythias went and anything Damon had Pythias could have, and the other way round. And you remember how the Tyrant of Syracuse threw Damon into prison and condemned him to death—those Tyrants were—well—simply tyrants—and as soon as Pythias heard of it, he hurried to the tyrant and said, "Don't execute Damon; execute me in his place." But Damon broke in and said to the tyrant, "You can't do that; you sentenced me first; execute me and let Pythias go." The tyrant was touched—deep down, he was all heart. He executed them both.

That was the story, or rather that was the first part of it. But if you have read Greek mythology you know that there was more. I shall never forget those lectures I took from Professor Dim on the mythology of Greece. "Wonderful!" I used often to wake up suddenly and say to myself, "fascinating."

As Professor Dim would explain to us that according to the Greeks, when two twin souls existed together like that, they were supposed to pass on after death, side by side, waiting, waiting to come together, and the Fates, all through the passing years, used to weave the skein of life—Professor Dim used to do actual weaving in the air, right in the classroom—and when the threads come together—their souls came back to human life again, and went through the same fate. There was a Greek name that Professor Dim gave to it, *metem*—something—it doesn't matter; I'll think of it in a minute.

But notice if the skein went wrong—if the black thread held by the dark goddess Morta, the one on the right, was woven in with the white—you could see Professor Dim actually weave it in, a thin black thread—that is you could see that he saw it, could just see it through his spectacles . . . Well—if this thin black thread mixed in—then, aha!—and that is what we are going to tell about.

But wait just a minute first. It occurs to me that I got it wrong about Damon and Pythias and what the Tyrant of Syracuse did. Of course he didn't execute them. It was the other way on. He was going to and then he was so touched with their devotion that he begged he might join in their friendship and make a third . . . That was it . . . and after that the three were just an inseparable trio . . . You'd see them together, at all the town gatherings, at all the public executions—there they were, arm in arm, laughing together.

Now years and years ago I knew Damon and Pythias personally; so did lots of people in the Canadian city where I lived. In fact, they hadn't been in the law school for a fortnight before everybody was saying, "There go Damon and

Pythias." Their names weren't *really* that—yet in a sort of a way their names half suggested it. You know the way some thing half suggests something! Professor Dim said the Greek called it—*Para*—ach! *para* something—I'll get it presently Anyway *their* names were Dannie Dament and Slugge Pethick. . . . They weren't in the least alike. Damon wa short and fair and bright and lively, with blue eyes that wer always changing and happy and restless. Slugger was a great big hulk of a fellow, lurched over at the top, dark as crime— say, he did look like a criminal! He didn't belong to the city as Dannie did. He'd just come from a small place, just a village, away out past Wiarton . . . You know what fellow look like when they come from past any place like Wiarton.

So please try to get the two clearly apart. Look at them there in the corridor of the law school, one each side of the professor as they just come out of a lecture . . . Dannie—he' so quick and easy and glib—is looking up sideways into the professor's face and saying, "I must congratulate you, sir, or a most brilliant lecture!" The nerve of him, eh? Of course it was a dangerous thing to do, because the professor—natu rally stopped in his tracks and said—"As a matter of fact, Mr Dament, there were several very interesting points under section 92, article eleven, which I really should have ex plained . . . You see" . . . And with that he began to expand, with Dannie looking brightly in his face like an at tentive bird, and not hearing a word . . .

Let him stand there till I explain who the two are. Hi expansion will contract abruptly when he looks round into Slugger's face.

Dannie Dament enjoyed a peculiar social prestige because his family had for generations been prominent people and also because his father had skipped off to the United States. I'm afraid some people now wouldn't quite understand what I mean by "skipping to the States." It was a way they used to go. Tourists? No, not exactly tourists. They just skipped across . . . It was their way of going.

And when they had skipped across to the United States you never heard of them for years and perhaps never again. Perhaps they committed suicide in a hotel—a little room with gaslight, a bed and a dresser . . . So Dannie's father, as everybody knew had skipped to the States—and was gone.

They all remembered him. Such a pleasant hearty man he was, Charles Edward Dament, that it was a pleasure to look at him; a large man, an imposing man, with a strong face that smiled, clean-shaven, behind his gold spectacles as fresh and bright as the morning . . . Add with it a Panama hat, and a loose summer suit of brown holland, a loose expensive tie, and all so clean and fresh and honest . . . Who wouldn't trust a man like that? And they all did. Why not, indeed? For the man was the soul of honour. Everybody knew that; and for that reason they put him on to every board, to every public charity, to every committee. He was the Treasurer of the Church of England Cathedral, Treasurer of the Art Museum, Treasurer of the Board of Education—in fact, of everything that had money. All the more so and especially as he never stinted money, never stinted salaries. There was plenty of money, he said, where money came from. Never was such a man for raising salaries! He raised all the clergy of the Cathedral—even the Bishop, his own personal friend (that wouldn't stop him), he raised him. He raised the teachers; he doubled the Budget of the Art Museum, and brought mummies all the way from Egypt, like so much cord wood.

And, mind you, a far-sighted man! A man who would look into the future! "Money, Dannie," he used to say, "money brings money. All you need, Dannie, is vision. Make money work and never grudge it; there's enough for all of them."

All round the city and just outside it Mr. Dament could see the empty waste places, and the mud flats and the sunken ravines filled with litter . . . He could see what that would mean when the city began to grow! Think of all that when the city would reach half a millon, yes, a million . . . A dream! No, sir, a reality.

And in went the money—into the dream. Half the endowment of the Cathedral into a mudflat . . . the funds of the Museum, and the endowment of four college chairs were sunk under the sand beside a creek half a mile from the city limits. "Vision!" he said, and he used to tell the Bishop about it through the cigar smoke—the Bishop and Colonel Strong the Chief Magistrate, and Judge Mildmay—all his old friend and fellow trustees. They'd been boys together at school. There was just one thing. Mr. Dament kept no accounts—or no separate accounts. He was, as he said, no bookkeeper. Everything went into his own account, in and out of it. That seemed to make it all the more secure, you see, because it made him responsible. In fact, as he said himself, it guaranteed everything.

So that was how it happened. We've seen it half a dozen times since, played out from start to finish; the slacking of good times, the slump, the squeeze, the crash! And then ruin . . . And Dament responsible to the law. There was no doubt of it; "misappropriation of funds"—it sounds bad doesn't it, when it's really vision.

They looked into it, privately at first—and Judge Mildmay said, "Charlie, I'm afraid you'll have to go" . . . and presently Colonel Strong said, "Charlie, I think you must go. We shall have to get out a *capias* but I can hold it till you're gone." Colonel Strong was a veteran of all the wars there had been and he wore all the ribbons that there were. He would never flinch from his duty, but he wanted to get Dament out of the way before he unflinched it. A *capias* meant a document, inviting a person, very warmly, not to leave the province. When a person "skipped to the States" it was the custom first to be sure that he'd got there and then get out a *capias*.

"Is the writ out for him?" asked the Bishop of Colonel Strong a night or so later.

"Not yet," said the Colonel. "I want to be quite sure first."

"I know that he got to"—the Bishop put up his hand and whispered—"Buffalo."

"Not far enough," said the Colonel . . . "There's always a danger of error if he's near the border."

"Where then?" the Bishop whispered. "Cleveland?"

"Too near the lake," said the Colonel. "I'd like him clear across Ohio."

A day or two later the Bishop whispered, "it's all right he's at . . ." The name went like a whispered sigh . . . Was it "Cincinnati?"

So they got out the *capias* forbidding Charles Edward Dament to leave the province.

So when he was gone, Mrs. Dament—Dannie's mother—took in boarders in the great big family house, which was her own—about all she had. At first it was very grand, quite distinguished and Mrs. Dament a sort of chatelaine, a person of prestige . . . "Boarding at Mrs. Dament's" sounded high class. Then, as the years went by, as the house grew shabby and the furniture rickety, the place became just like any other "boarding house," and the boarders just boarders. "They say her husband skipped to the States years ago," an old boarder would say to a new, and the new boarder just answer, "He did, eh?" And as the years went by and the "landlady" (Mrs. Dament) grew old and worn—careworn—the boarder would answer, "He did, eh? Can you blame him?" That was a boarding house joke. Boarding houses were cruel places.

So can you wonder that Dannie Dament, with all those wonderful "advantages of adversity" that the socialists describe, grew up bright and self reliant and helpful? How could he help it with such a father? But, of course, they didn't know all this time where Dament's father was—or weren't told. Some people said that he had committed suicide in a hotel in Cincinnati—or in a hotel somewhere. They often did, those who skipped and mostly in hotels. People disliked it elsewhere . . . But this was just talk. At any rate Judge Mildmay and the Bishop and Colonel Strong, Dannie's father's friends, if they knew, took care not to tell. If they had, then, you see, Dannie and his mother would have to *know*. Do you get it? As long as they didn't know, that blocked all legal inquiry looking to extradition. They could, if need be, swear—oh, what is it you call it—a *nescio quod,* meaning I don't know anything, or sign, both of them an *ignoramus.* They didn't know, and after Dannie's mother had gone—she died the sixth year after—Dannie knew still less . . . As a matter of fact, no one knew. That was Dannie Dament.

Slugger Pethick was very different. He'd had no advantages, brought up rough, away off in the country, somewhere back of Wiarton. You know what that would be like. He had no decent chance to learn what was right and what was wrong, not out there, with his father just a Church of England rural clergyman in a place of about five hundred people. As I say, he had no way of knowing right from wrong. When he came down he was wearing a celluloid collar—didn't know it was wrong; and when he met anybody he used to say, "Pleased to meet you," and start to pull off his gloves, even if he didn't have any on—the way they do back of Wiarton . . . And he wore a "dicky" on Sundays (you know what that is) and thought it pretty slick . . . A lot of that he never lost. They never do, the people away back in the country, no matter how celebrated they get—prime ministers, bankers, statesmen, it doesn't matter—you notice them still pulling off gloves that aren't there, and see them unconsciously fumbling at their necks. They're feeling at their celluloid collar to see if their tie is still there—the little ten-cent tie that hooked on with elastic.

Slugger's father, I say, was just a little country clergyman, short, wiry, tanned and worn. He was a "horse and buggy" clergyman, for on Sunday, after he'd preached in his own place in the morning—it was called, what was it? Something— Head—he drove out seven miles to take an out-of-town service at another place; seven miles out and seven back. Devoted work, you say? Well, yes, that's right, but of course he got fifty-two dollars for it. Fifty-two dollars a Sunday? Oh, no, no; fifty-two dollars a year—a dollar a Sunday. It made a big difference. Of course, mind you, he got his supper—they had to give him that—and he got his oats and he got his hay, and of course he got a rub any time. It worked pretty well. So with his hay and oats what more could he ask? At any rate he didn't.

Arthur Pethick, years and years before, had been at school,

boarding school with Dannie's father, all the way from the third form to the sixth—and they had been great friends. But their studies were different. Arthur Pethick took Greek which led him in due course into the Church of England. Charlie Dament took mathematics which led in due course to the United States.

With the Reverend Arthur Pethick, sharing his labours, was his wife, a little wiry nut-brown woman who "did all her own work," watched her husband's thankless and unending toil, and hated religion like hell. To Slugger she was "mother," and it was the unstilled anger in her soul, no doubt, that had put that heavy shadow across his face.

Yet it was amazing how fast Slugger Pethick got on at law school. It was Rugby football that first did it. They played in those days the real old Rugby with the tight scrimmage and with Slugger as centre scrimmage the thing just turned to massacre. That's where Slugger got his nickname. It was changed over from his real name, which was merely, just the simple old English "Slaughter." The Law School moved up to first place in the Union, with wild excitement at the games, and even the senior judges running up and down along the touch line under the trees. There was no stadium then; admission was all free; the judges attended constantly.

So Slugger Pethick moved on. He moved out of his celluloid collar, for he caught on that he and the Chief Justice were the only ones who wore them. He met at different houses the sisters of fellow students. (That's how you get educated fast.) He gave private tuition to a rich man's son who couldn't learn anything except for money, bought a dress suit and a big dress shirt with cuffs as large as a book, went to dances, couldn't dance but didn't need to—the girls said he looked "saturnine," and that was enough.

It was during their last years at the Law School, in fact during the final examinations, that there came to Damon Dament and Pythias Pethick the first of those strange—how shall we say—strange quiverings of the strings of destiny that came to them all the way down from Ancient Syracuse.

It was in connection with their being accused of cheating—of "copying"—in one of the final examinations.

Such accusations—such deeds themselves—are now long since past. We are speaking of times of a lower standard. All examinations now in colleges and in law school are conducted on the "honour system." All the students are on their honour not to copy. They go into the exam room on their honour and they come out still on their honour, so they can't have copied. But in any case the examiners are on their honour not to watch them. It is what is called Student Control.

But in these earlier days it was "catch as catch can" and any student could copy if he wouldn't get caught; but, mind you, only from his friends or from students he knew. Otherwise you couldn't tell what you were copying. Well, anyway, Dannie and Peth were summoned from the exam room in the Law School to the Judges' Chambers and there stood Justice Mildmay with two senior examiners and he had in his hands the papers they had written the day before.

"Gentlemen," he said, "I am deeply grieved to send for you, but your papers of yesterday have been submitted to me and there can be no doubt that they show unmistakable evidence of copying. One of you, I regret to say, stands guilty."

There was a moment's pause and then Dannie Dament looked up and said:

"I did it. The fault is entirely mine. Pethick had nothing to do with it."

The judge looked at him with mingled sorrow and admiration, and regret—for his father's sake . . .

"This is very honourable of you, very honourable Mr. Dament," he began, but the Slugger broke in:

"Judge Mildmay, I copied that paper. I want no one to shield me—I'll look after myself," and he gave a dark look towards the two examiners that made them jump.

"Please don't listen," pleaded Dannie (he had a wonderful face for that sort of thing).

Judge Mildmay paused. He was really touched.

"Gentlemen," he said, "this is indeed magnanimous; one of you is telling a most noble truth, the other a most noble lie. If you recall your classics, gentlemen, I will remind you of Damon and Pythias . . . I must ask you to wait outside a few moments, gentlemen, till we reach a decision."

A few moments later Dannie and the Slugger came skipping down the outside steps, absolved, exonerated, elevated.

"It worked all right," said Dannie.

"Certainly did," said Slugger.

And it was all over town in a day or two. In Ancient Syracuse, in the land of the Shades, they knew it that same evening.

It was for that reason and similar ones that Dannie Dament and Slugger Pethick made such an immediate success when they "put up their shingle" that autumn as *Dament and Pethick—Barristers, Solicitors etc."* How could they fail anyway? They were so well matched. Dannie was so bright and

winning that the judges couldn't help giving him a decision
. . . and Slugger Pethick was so large and fierce that the
judges were afraid of him . . . Dannie naturally leaned to
the civil side, so smooth and coy, that every plea seemed
convincing. But Slugger took criminal work, particularly
with juries. Give him a criminal to defend, as tough looking
as himself, and let him say, "I defy any intelligent man in
this jury—my client defies them—to dare to impute . . ."
And when the foreman said "not guilty" and the clerk asked,
"And so say all of you?" they yelled out a chorus of "Yes,
yes," each wanting to be first . . .

Success? Why, of course, no end of it. In the very first year
the Slugger was able to send home to "mother" back of Wiarton a sewing machine—and a washing machine and an iron-
ing machine—presents dear to the heart of people like
"mother" who did her own work and could thus do twice as
much work in double the time. Success! Why Dannie joined
the Yacht Club without a yacht, the golf Club without a club
—or the Art Association without a brush. It's the "joining"
that does it. They succeeded so fast that within a year or two
they moved into a large suite of offices, all leather and books,
with a big room like a board room—in fact they called it that.
They needed this room for their private practice outside the
courts. For they soon found, as all lawyers do, that there is
no real money in chasing little suits in and out of law courts.
There may be money in huge suits where two huge companies, both crooked, are driven along, both fighting, by a
group of lawyers, prodding them to make them fight more.
You may have seen pictures of those huge primitive animals
(I think Professor Dim used to call them dinosaurs) being
prodded along towards a huge pit by primitive huntsmen
with steel goads . . . Well, that's like the companies in law-

suits, prodded slowly towards the Privy Council, or the Su-
preme Court, or any Final Court of Appeal . . .

But short of that the little stuff is no good. The thing is
to get the cases settled out of court—get both the litigants to
meet in a friendly way in a big office, all luxury and leather,
make them feel formal and uncomfortable; then insist on
their having a glass of sherry, out of a wainscot cupboard;
that gets them comfortable . . .

The custom of the office was that Dannie, in the discussion,
would represent one side, fairly and dispassionately—but still
representing one side. He was speaking, let us say, for the
claim of Mr. Smith. "I doubt," he would say, "and Mr. Smith
admits that I am speaking *ex-parte*"—Mr. Smith nodded—he
didn't know what it meant; but that was him. And Slugger
said, "I feel that Mr. Jones is absolutely right—indeed I insist that he's right in claiming"—and so on.

And then came the mystic message all down the skeins of
destiny from Ancient Syracuse and Dannie would change
sides and say, "That's right; we're wrong there . . ." And
the Pethick changed sides with "No, no, we're willing to
withdraw"—and so on.

A few minutes later their two litigants went down the stairs
into the sunlight, dazed . . . "Couple of crooks!" one mut-
tered as they went out. "I don't know," the other reflected.
"I thought it very generous minded when they turned round
like that, it reminded me"—he paused, but couldn't think
what is was, and the other had stopped listening anyway.

Municipal politics came next. I don't mean immediately.
Of course, meantime, the years went flowing past, and the
birds sang and the city grew and the Slugger sent his father
a top buggy and a set of harness and a pair of horse blankets

(things needed for church work) and got his mother a kitchen range and an Indian girl—as help, I mean. She wouldn't consider a white one. "They're asking ten dollars," she said, and it was ridiculous . . .

So naturally they went into city politics. It just came of itself. The firm was so popular. In due time a group of organizers in Ward Six came to Dannie Dament and said that if he would run for the City Council the nomination was his for the asking. He had hardly accepted when another group of voters nominated Slugger Pethick. Next day the papers announced that Mr. Dament has withdrawn his name in favour of that of Mr. Pethick and the day after that Mr. Pethick had withdrawn his in favour of Mr. Dament. The wide comment on this magnanimity in withdrawing in Ward Three led to their being elected separately in Ward Four and Ward Five.

These were busy, busy days for the City Council. Science had taken hold of municipal enterprise. The entire city was to be repaved with the newly invented cedar-block-tar-and-gravel pavement. It made a pavement just as smooth—well, just as smooth as tar and gravel—guaranteed to last five years, and not to last longer. It would take five years to pave the city and at the end of five years they would begin again. There would be no end of the paving.

Applications for paving contracts fell like snowflakes on the counsellors' desks. The newspapers soon announced that Counsellor Dament has made his policy in the matter of pavement contracts quite clear. "I propose," he said, "to make no distinction in this matter between friends and enemies. I see no reason why I should refuse a contract to a personal friend." It was similarly announced that Counsellor Pethick had said, "I shall be glad to assign contracts even to my personal enemies." So they gave them right and left to both . . . And all the city smelt fresh with new-cut cedar, and warm with tar . . . and you could hear the thump-thump of pile-drivers miles out in the fields where there were no houses at all—only streets and birds.

So the years went by and the seasons came and went, and the birds sang, and the city grew and life moved on and on . . . The city grew and grew; how amazingly it began to expand; new streets all leafy with young chestnut trees and fresh with beds of tulips where nothing had been but waste land and ash heaps . . . bridges tracing their way through the tree tops of the sunken ravines and all the dust and sand, the hollows and the mudflats, where lay buried the funds of the Cathedral and the endowment of the Art Museum turning into a very bower of beauty and secluded charm.

It was while walking in these days in the suburbs of the city that there came to Dannie Dament the great idea of "vindicating his father's memory." That's what he called it; proving to the world that his father's "vision" had been justi-fied. The idea was to buy in all the old claims, the mortgage-ridden equities, the properties seized for taxes—buy it all in and as the value rose pay back the lost endowment of the church, interest and all; re-upholster the four college chairs, redeem the mummies, and—this part of it Dannie didn't say out loud (or only to Pethick)—pocket the difference. It is one of the great principles of large scale philanthropy.

It was a delicate matter. It could only be done with great caution. Real estate had been "dead" but only in the sense that an Arkansas mule is sometimes dead. Real estate sleeps with one eye open. So they moved carefully; bought in and bought back and bought out what they could as a matter of routine . For the rest they used long range methods, done by careful advertising. As for instance:

Country Clergyman, about to retire would buy small empty lot in north of city; sand preferred.

Country clergyman, chronic invalid, would buy site for cottage and orchard in north outskirts of city; no objection to spring floods; will take mud.

The country clergyman was, of course—though he never saw the advertisements—the Rev. Arthur Pethick, of Something-Head beyond Wiarton. He signed and sent purchases and re-sales by the same mail, thinking them merely instalments of something. Clergymen in the country sign so many instalments that they cease to read them.

Those who deal with suckers are themselves suckers. Dannie soon found he could pitch the advertisements to as high a note as he liked, make them as glaring as a glass window. No one saw through.

Country clergyman, about to retire, in possession of funds of own and other clergy—all simple and without experience—would like to buy wide tract of sand, dirt or mud—anywhere near city.

In return for this and with his father's memory in mind, Dannie helped to advance the Slugger's father—advance his status in the church. Dannie's influence with the aging Bishop raised the Reverend Arthur Pethick from a rector to a rural dean. The difference between these lies in a different cord on the hat and a different shade of ecclesiastical functions rather hard to define. But call it fifty dollars a year. Soon after that, Rural Dean Pethick was raised to be a Canon,

as of the Cathedral but extra-parochial, or extra-something—
at any rate, extra pay. This time it meant a solid five hundred dollars a year so that the Rev. Canon Pethick was able
to hire a divinity student to rub down his horse and take it
out for country sermons while "mother" prepared a special
supper for the Canon. The Canon paid the divinity student
six hundred a year. As a matter of fact Canon Pethick himself went out most Sundays; the people expected it; the divinity student ate the supper.

It was at that stage of Dannie Dament's vindication of his
father's memory that Dannie's father suddenly ceased to be a
memory and became a fact.

Judge Mildmay sent for Dannie one morning to his chambers.

The Judge was ageing slowly but surely, as even judges do.
When he read he stooped his spectacles down close to the
paper or held the paper far from his spectacles with one
hand . . . To listen, he put one hand to his ear, or didn't
listen at all. But of course he could still decide law suits—
large ones, appeal cases—by instinct.

"Dannie," he said, and the paper rustled in his hand, "I
have heard from your father . . ."

"My father," Dannie said; only that—he couldn't say more.

"After all these years," said the judge, "I have heard from
him. He's in Cincinnati."

"Cincinnati," said Dannie; just that.

"He wrote me—but the details might distress you—he has
managed to support himself . . ."

"Support himself," repeated Dannie.

". . . By keeping books in a factory. You will recall,"

the judge continued, "his singular aptitude for keeping books . . ."

Dannie didn't. Nor was there any to recall. But it didn't matter . . . A bookkeeper in a factory; Dannie had a vision of some little end room partitioned in with boards, a wood stove standing on end and in a corner a high desk and ledgers, and the boss saying, "This is Mr. Dament, our bookkeeper, gents; Charlie, have you got them files of the year before last . . ."

"He wishes to know"—and the papers rustled again—"if the situation of things, if the law, or rather the lapse of time—in short—if he can come home . . ."

"Come home—" Dannie repeated, and as his mind began to work again he added, "Can he?"

"There is nothing to stop him," said Judge Mildmay, "there never was; only that if he came the debts would still be there . . . and, I speak plainly—not only the debts. Those are nothing, to a man who has nothing to pay with—but the charge of embezzlement . . . that never sleeps."

"If the debts were paid?"

"The charge would fall of itself—or could be made to. *Res ipsa loquitur*," added the judge, to make his meaning quite clear.

"Do you know how much they are?"

"We have them all here, all filed. A great sum they seemed then but in these days everything has moved so fast, no doubt not so formidable . . . I'll say, at a guess, two hundred thousand dollars."

The judge's guess was based on having added up the items about five minutes before.

"Judge," said Dannie, "give me six months more of this

real estate market and I can pay it five times over—then he can come back, eh?"

"In any case," said the judge, "it would take six months. There are certain legal formalities. We have to petition the Crown." He fell to musing. "You must see that no proceedings are started in the interim . . . See the chief creditors—there are only a few after all . . ." The judge's fingers rustled and trembled among the papers; "The Bishop, as representing the Synod of the Church . . . Colonel Strong for the Museum of Art, and the University, one or two others; that's all. The smaller claims were brought up. I think Mr. Sheppardson holds most of them . . ."

So in the ensuing weeks Dannie saw the creditors.

"Why, said the Bishop, "of course! My oldest friend. He would be welcomed with affection . . . Forgive us our debts, Dannie, as we forgive our debtors."

It appeared it was a point of Christian doctrine that all debts, when paid in full with compound interest at six per cent, should be forgiven and forgotten. As the Bishop explained, we have St. Paul's authority for it, and Timothy's, also—good enough security for Dannie.

Dannie saw Colonel Strong, now heartier, ruddier, haler than ever, taking his middle seventies in a stride that had not yet slackened—more medals on him than ever and another war to the good.

"Leave it to me, Dannie . . . I'll fix it," he said.

The only other chief representative of the creditors was old Mr. Sheppardson. It was his special business to represent creditors—or, rather, to buy up their credit. Particularly he dealt in widows and orphans—people unable to look after themselves. It was the business of Mr. Sheppardson's firm to look after them—to see that they didn't lose everything of the little they had. It was Mr. Sheppardson's policy to see that widows and orphans were always certain of getting something, by buying their claims from them for less than nothing.

And now Dannie turned again to the real estate market with a new purpose to make it move, to get the debts paid, to bring his father home in honour. He could see himself meeting his father at the railway station; he could hear his father's resonant laugh, his merry greeting! Just let that market move and the thing would be done.

And did it move? And what so merry as a real estate market when it *does* move? The real estate people have their own names for such a market—recovering—active—lively— buoyant—and at length, like the rest of us, it just goes wild. Great sport! To buy by the acre and sell by the foot! To put in ten dollars today and call it twenty tomorrow and a hundred next week! To buy options on land reaching away out among the farms, to run street lines through the pastures and indicate the routes of electric street cars! Take all that, with spring weather, and April showers and sunshine—what scenery is ever so beautiful as real estate scenery, with theodolites in every open field, and surveyors' links trailing in the grass.

There was in those days, as we have said, a recognized and orthodox way of "skipping to the States." So, too, there was the recognized procedure of a triumphant return. There was always the dinner given to the creditors with a cheque under each plate, and champagne—speeches—Dannie had it all rehearsed in his mind. The Slugger's father, the Rev. Arthur Pethick, must be there. He was not a creditor but they could give him a cheque anyway, and take it away again afterwards. He wouldn't know the difference—and, of course, Mr. Sheppardson, if only to have him tell, as part of his speech on such occasions, his standard narrative of the "poor little woman," the little widow all in black, who came into his office, scarcely daring to hope—but there, sure enough, was every dollar she had entrusted to them ten years before and it had turned into a dollar fifteen. Oh, yes, a wonderful dinner it would be, especially his father's speech—his father had been wonderful on speeches.

Would you believe it, Dannie had the dinner all arranged with the caterer months ahead; in fact, the day after he spoke to the judge.

So there!—and just as everything was moving like that, the skeins of fate noiselessly weaving, parted—and something happened. We recall Professor Dim and that little black thread that gets woven into the skein of fate by the Dark Goddess. Well, here is just where she found the opportunity to weave it in. And the dark thread was—it always is—a woman.

The Honorable Mrs. Fordeck had just come out from England to the city and was for the moment the whole thing in social circles. She was what women called a fine looking woman and what men by instinct keep away from. She loved to refer to herself as a soldier's daughter but in reality she looked closer to being a soldier's mother or aunt—at least that. She had that type of face that good birth gives either to a women or a horse. And birth she certainly had. There was not doubt about her superior birth. She was the niece of the Earl of Haddock of Haddock Castle where she had spent most of her life—as a "ghell"—and, where all the gillies and the crofters—she loved to explain it herself—were simply devoted to her.

But at the time when Mrs. Fordeck used to stay at Haddock Castle she was just a very young girl, because as she explained, with the greatest candour, she was married before she was really old enough to know anything about anything. Her husband—her first husband—was in the Buffs—poor Jack, that was long ago. He died in the Chitral—Mrs. Fordeck didn't say of drink. Her second husband she loved to speak of as "poor Harry Fordeck." He was an American, from Cincinnati, but his people really were very good people—none of them came from America. Happy, happy years!—that's what Mrs. Fordeck loved to call them. Those were the days when she was simply fascinated—you know how a woman like that says "simply fascinated"—with Africa, with lion hunting. She went there first just after Jack's death because it helped to divert her thoughts from her loss. When you hunt lions, it seems, your thoughts never wander. And after that she went, as she said, year after year.

So when she married poor Harry Fordeck she took him with her to Africa, although he was much older than she was and really too old for lion hunting. It was foolish not to have guarded him better. She couldn't blame herself enough. But it all happened so suddenly. There were a number of lions in a nullah just beyond a kloof on the Karoo—the words are those of Mrs. Fordeck, or close to them—and the beaters were leading the party in Indian file through tall millet to keep out of sight and avoid them. When they got through poor Harry was gone. Mrs. Fordeck implied that they could actually hear the lions eating Harry but that it was too painful to dwell upon.

It was just while the surveyors were out in the April sunshine creating real estate values with a theodolite that the
Honorable Mrs. Fordeck met Dannie Dament and Slugger
Pethick. She met them at an evening reception where they
had gone to look for real estate. She met them and hooked
them both. I mean that Dannie Dament and Slugger Pethick
both "fell for her" just as easily as that. Both of them
together.

You see, you can't have all the kinds of smartness and all
the kinds of common sense at once. There was something
about "nobility"—I mean about being connected with nobility—that hit Dannie and Pethick where they lived. It
naturally does hit anyone who lives beyond Wiarton, or even
anyone living above College Street, Toronto. They say it
can reach clear to Texas.

Mrs. Fordeck got them both at one shot by thus meeting
them both together at an evening reception. They knew she
was the niece of an Earl and it made them both shy. Even
Dannie's lights faded dim and Slugger Pethick pulled off
gloves he didn't have on and said, "pleased to meet you," as
clumsily as the day he left Something-Head. The phrase is,
of course, not one to be used to a lady with a title. It should
be kept for society beyond Wiarton where they take pleasure
in one another's society. People of birth don't.

Anyway they were hooked. Mrs. Fordeck said they might
take her to get an ice. They did. And when she said, "Now
tell me what on earth am I to do with fifty thousand pounds?"
they nearly dropped their plates! So Mrs. Fordeck laughed
and said—"Oh, I don't mean my own. I'd know jolly well
what to do with it if it was my own. I'd be off to Africa with
it like a shot. But I mean here's this wretched old uncle of
mine (I mean Lord Haddock, though he really isn't half

bad)—here he is with an idea that this is a country of wonderful opportunity."

Oh, say! Did they pile up the ice cream near her! And did they wheel arm chairs for her! And Dannie laughed that pleasant laugh of his and Pethick rubbed his big hands . . . and Mrs. Fordeck told them about the lions, and poor Harry . . . and the Buffs and the Chitral, and her friendship with the Prince of Wales (meaning of course *the* Prince of Wales) and how, when she was with him, she sometimes liked the Prince and sometimes didn't, but really she thought that in her heart—her own nature—she liked plainer people, more direct people, people with simpler ways.

Oh, yes, they fell fast enough. They made an appointment for her to come to the office. They would look after the fifty thousand pounds with pleasure.

One may ask why didn't such shrewd lawyers as Dament and Pethick look up the standing of the Earl of Haddock. The answer is that they did look him up and were deeper out of their depth than ever. There they sat, one each side of the table in their big Board Room, Dannie with Debrett's *Peerage* and Slugger with *Who's Who,* looking up the Earl of Haddock.

"Here you have it?" says Dannie, "Edgar Gaulter De Prothero Ross Haddock, Fifteenth Earl of Haddock—Fifteenth? Oh, boy!—born so and so, succeeded so and so, seat Haddock Castle, Caithness (do you get that? He has a "seat") estates also in Ross and Cromarty."

"And hear this," said Slugger, "served Cold Guards (*Cold* Guards? What are they?), 2nd Burmese, Relief of Kumasi,

Relief of Poonah, Relief of Khartum, Medal and Four Clasps, Grand Star of Burma, Grand Cross of Egpyt."

"Went up the Irrawaddy," read out Dannie. "Does your book say that? And up the Blue Nile—no, up the Niger."

"Some soldier, eh," they both said, and Dannie read on: "Hereditary Equerry of the Buckhounds, Order of the Thistle, Keeper of the County Purse—You get that do you?"

"Yes and listen. Recreations: fencing, lion hunting (that's where she gets that) and—get this—capturing big snakes . . . Those are his *recreations*, eh?"

They read it all as innocently as children, clean out of their field. What would they know of wind-swept estates of heather and gorse and moor, with broken rocks falling to the sea, of a flock of "gillies" and "crofters"; gillies who "gill" for nothing and crofters who "croft" for crofting's sake—till in despair they emigrate to Northwest Canada, singing *Lochaber no More*. How could they picture a tumbled castle, all wind and draft and faded wainscotting with waving rags called tapestry, where a threadbare butler as ancient as his clothes, serves upon silver a gallant old soldier as threadbare as himself. Lions? Yes, forty years ago. Biography knows no difference.

They not only hunted the Earl up in the books but they found a pretext to go and ask old Mr. Sheppardson about him, old Sheppardson being the chairman of the Stock Exchange, the head of the chief financial firm and the last word in intimate finance. The reader may recall him as he's been mentioned already in this book—when he had tears in his eyes over his son-in-law's money. He always had tears in his eyes. He did his business on tears.

"The Earl of Haddock," said Mr. Sheppardson, "has been deeply interested in Canada for years. Indeed he has sent many of his crofters to Manitoba. I managed it for him. Now as to his private investment"—Mr. Sheppardson put the points of his fingers together and there were no tears in his eyes—"that, of course, is a matter on which, as you readily understand—exactly . . . One thing, perhaps, I *may* say, and I will say—or perhaps on second thought I *won't* say . . . He might—you understand, he *might* . . ."

But Mr. Sheppardson had said quite enough to make them enthusiastic.

"I must say," continued Mr. Sheppardson, "that when Mrs. Fordeck came to see me, I was deeply moved, deeply touched. Her husband you know, poor Harry Fordeck, was eaten by lions. They were moving, it seems, through tall millet in a nullah, across the Karoo, single file to avoid the lions. Fordeck missed the path and must have got among the lions. The poor lady told me—it brought tears to my eyes—that they could actually hear the crunching."

"We know, we know," said the partners, and with that they hurried away.

"Mrs. Fordeck," said Dannie, "is certainly a most striking woman."

"I call her handsome," said the Slugger, in a tone of challenge.

"Yes," asserted Dannie, "in fact, I'd call her a fine looking woman."

They were both lying and they knew it. The Dark Goddess was weaving in the black thread as fast as her fingers could travel, and the fair Goddess on the left, Nona, who stands for life and happiness, dropped tears upon the skein.

But the main mischief was done that September at a big dance given at Colonel Strong's house. In those days when they gave a dance they didn't have it done by proxy—a hotel management arranging the occasion, a chef arranging the food, a florist the flowers, an orchestra the music and a secretary arranging the guests. That isn't giving a dance. That's signing a cheque.

In those days when people gave a dance they *gave* a dance—and they always gave their dances in private houses, especially in those beautiful old houses that stood, all lawn and leaves, in half an acre of ground. Colonel Strong's house was like that, and he had enough granddaughters and grand-nieces on, and in reach of, the premises to put any dance off to a good start.

Take such a house on a September evening, one of those mellow, soft September evenings, with leaves still so heavy that for people in the houses they half hid the street lights and turned them into fire-flies—like fairyland; a great house all balconies, and conservatories and odd corners, and secluded spots, turned into veritable man-traps with masses of ferns and chrysanthemums, by the hands of the grand-nieces and granddaughters. Pretty dangerous place, eh? And for less sentimental hearts there were sideboards with refreshments, great rounds of cold beef looking out from parsley—pink hams from some once giant hog, and all of it flanked with bottled ale, claret cup in stone jars, and lighter stuff like Moselle and champagne, standing in tubs of ice.

Dangerous! At least Dannie and Pethick were to find it so, separately and jointly.

One didn't do much actual dancing in those days, except the quite young. All hands from the host and hostess down joined in the square dances, the lancers and the quadrilles, but a lot of the older people were soon playing whist in quiet card rooms. And the marriageable girls "sitting out" out on balconies, and asking about the stars.

Dannie could never remember, though he tried hard, afterwards, just what it was that he said to Mrs. Fordeck that evening. They were behind a huge hydrangea bush in a tub on a balcony in low chairs with a little table to which Dannie had brought the champagne. Those are hard places from which to remember things accurately. Did Mrs. Fordeck say that the scene was just like Capetown, and did Dannie say that he had always longed to see Capetown (a dirty lie), and did she say, "Some day I hope you will?" It seems likely that she did. And it was then that Mrs. Fordeck had said that she had come to regard him as something far different from just her lawyer. Did she say "as something far nearer?" Yes, I guess she did. Did Dannie say something about something nearer still? He may have. And then she said something about its being too wonderful, and that he must let her wait a few days to give him her answer.

Pethick remembered better. He had sat in behind a grapevine with cold chicken and Moselle. Mrs. Fordeck had said: "Doesn't this heavenly night remind you of Capetown?"

He had answered, "Wiarton is very much like this in September," and she said, "I should just *love* to see Wiarton," and he said, "I hope you will some day. I could give you a letter to Bill Furze, the postmaster, and he'd show you round," and he had added, "If I was up there, I'd like to show you round myself . . ." and then it was that Mrs. Fordeck had said that he meant more to her than just a lawyer. And she promised him his answer for a few days later.

Just at the close of the evening they were all three together, seated beside a buffet, and Mrs. Fordeck has said, "You're both just too wonderful. How I wish I could say 'yes' to both of you. But whichever way I decide, I shall always feel—" and so on to that effect.

Now here is where a message from Ancient Syracuse should have come down the shaking skeins to say, "Give her up! Each give her up!" There was a sort of message to that effect but it wasn't exactly from Syracuse. You see, after all, even if Mrs. Fordeck was a striking woman, even if marrying her meant stepping into a castle—even at all that—for a young man's fancy—for a young man's dream of love—well, not quite. Be fair, though. Either one would have taken her. There was no Damon and no Pythias that evening. The black thread was running fast into the skein.

There was, we say, no renunciation that evening—no Damon and Pythias stuff. But it came a few days later, all right enough. When they sat down in their office that morning, Dannie said.

"Peth, I've had time to think this thing over. I want you to marry Mrs. Fordeck. I'll stand aside and I hope you may be very happy."

There come to many men in life moments when they find themselves compelled to do the big thing, the generous thing. It seems as if they had no choice. Renunciation of self is, after all, one of the highest things of which we are capable. That may have been Dannie Dament's feeling on this morning when the came down to the office with his mind made up. It may have been or it may not.

Peth shook his head.

"It's fine of you, Dannie. You've spoken first, I admit, but

I had it here (he touched his pocket) in a letter already to give you. Take her, Dannie—she's yours, and some day after you're married I'll come over to Scotland and visit you at the big castle."

Minds attuned together as theirs were easily make contacts. The words "the big castle" were enough. Dannie began slowly to smile.

"I wonder if you have been reading what I have?" he asked.

"If you put it that way," said Pethick with a grin, "I guess I have."

"You mean," said Dannie, *"Pauper Peers."*

"That's it."

In the last mails from England there had just come over one of those *Chit-Chat* magazines that were just coming into fashion, full of Tom-Tit stuff, all about the underside of the upper side. Well, anyway, here was an article on *Our Pauper Peers.* It told how one of them played a street organ in London, how another was a pavement artist, and how the estates of some of them, in Scotland especially, were just waste land, with the crofters and such being starved out of them and going to Kansas and Manitoba. It mentioned the Earl of Haddock, and Haddock Castle, which was low, but so were all the Tom-Tit papers. The article said that the Earl wasn't worth a hundred pounds a year—put him at about eighty.

After that Dannie and Pethick waited for a blow to fall, feeling that there was a blow coming. All day they were out in the happy autumn fields of real estate where they were laying out Haddock Park but changing its name now to Ohio Garden; and all this time they were arranging with Judge Mildmay the legal formalities which were needed to bring Dannie's father home, and waiting for the blow.

Then it fell.

It fell as quietly as blows often fall. It was just a visit from old Mr. Sheppardson who came quietly down to their offices for what he called a purely friendly discussion. He was acting, he said, on Mrs. Fordeck's behalf but solely, as he explained, as a friend of all parties concerned. The poor lady, he said, had been deeply distressed. She had come into his office all in black (Mr. Sheppardson put that in by habit; as a matter of fact she was in blue). "You may have learned, I gather you have," said Mr. Sheppardson, "of the poverty of her family and especially of her uncle Lord Haddock. She took for granted that as men of honour"—(she is a soldier's daughter, Mr. Sheppardson added)—"as men of honour you knew it already" (That was a nasty tweeze for both of them.) "In short," said Mr. Sheppardson. . . . Well, in short, when he had done with it, what he meant was that one of them would darned well marry Mrs. Fordeck and the other give her twenty thousand dollars—or else—he didn't need to complete it. With that he withdrew.

At that time and place nothing struck terror to the human heart of the male like a breach of promise suit. It carried with it a peculiar measure of dishonour, not unconnected with a sort of comic element that made it the most dreaded form of disgrace. The shadow of Bardell vs. Picwick lay heavy across it. Hence Slugger in his dreams went through scenes in which a cross-examining barrister said:

"Answer the question, please, without evasion. Did you, or did you not, on the evening of September twelfth compare Capetown to Wiarton? You did? very good; I thought we should get at it at last; now, did you or did you not say, etc. etc."

And Dannie Dament also heard in his sleep the voice of the prosecuting counsel:

"Did the petitioner offer you the statement that you were something more to her than a lawyer—"

And himself, attempting to be facetious: *Something less—"*

Then the Court: *"I must ask you to abstain from any attempt at jocularity. Answer the question."*

Counsel, continuing: "Did you say that you hoped you were nearer to her than that?"

Himself: *"I did."*

Counsel: *"And how near were you to her at the time?"*

Then the courtroom in a roar."

No, no, they couldn't stand the disgrace, the laughter of it. In fact they knew, Dament and Pethick, Barristers etc., both of them, knew, that that kind of thing in that kind of town at that time would knock them both out of business, out of law, out of anything . . . In short, if the thing was pushed to the worst there was only one thing to do and they knew it. Marry Mrs. Fordeck? No, no, you've forgotten the beginning of this story—skip to the United States.

Here then was the irony of history! Dannie's father ready to come back, and Dannie ready to skip. "They can't stop us, can they Peth?" said Dannie, "if we decide to clear out?"

"Not without a *capias*," said the Slugger, "and they can't get a *capias* without a judgment to get it on, and before they get that we'll be gone. But you had better move fast, Dannie; there'll be a lot to do . . ."

Then fate intervened again.

Pethick came to the office next morning to find Dannie

with a telegram in his hand. "We're too late, Peth," Dannie said. "Father's arriving at eleven o'clock this morning."

Then he added, "You go, if you like." But Peth shook his head. The contact with Syracuse was working again.

Dannie somehow missed his father at the station—perhaps his father hadn't understood, the new station was so confusing. But he found him when he came back to the office, sitting there, with Canon Pethick, who had just arrived from Something-Head. His father! Could it really be his father! So changed, so broken—why, an old man! Can seventeen years do that? Is that from bookkeeping? Is that the kind of place that Cincinnati is?

"Father!" said Dannie, and he couldn't speak.

"We were just speaking," said Canon Pethick, "of some of the men we remember years ago." (Why, certainly; what else do old men talk of?)

So there they sat, as Dannie moved, heart-sick, about his office, exchanging their reminiscences . . . "But surely you must remember so and so? Why, of course; he played football,"—"No, no, that was his brother, the one who drank, and went into the church afterwards—did very well." And so on endlessly.

Dannie presently took them out to lunch, still talking reminiscences and seeing nothing. Then he left them to go and find Slugger who was away out somewhere in a field selling a site for a church.

And when Dannie came back with Slugger in the middle of the afternoon, the two old men were still talking, still twittering away at their reminiscences: "I wonder what became of so and so?" or, "Did any body ever hear anything of such and such . . ."

Dannie stood beside them, along with Slugger Pethick, deep in trouble and perplexity, scarcely hearing what they said. Then all of a sudden his father said something that made Dannie's mouth fall wide open with surprise, with sudden fixed attention. It was something amazing, something inconceivable.

"You remember," Mr. Dament was saying to the Canon—"you remember, though it is not his present name, and I shouldn't mention it for it might mean trouble for him. You remember Harry Fordeck?"

"Why, of course," said the Canon, "he was on the cricket team. Let me see, did I hear, didn't someone say he was dead years ago? Yes, yes, he was killed by lions in Africa. He was out with a big lion hunting party, moving (I remember distinctly hearing all about it) through a growth of tall millet . . ."

Mr. Dament shook his head.

"No, no," he said, "poor Harry. He's not dead. He's alive. He's in Cincinnati. I got him a job there with me as assistant bookkeeper . . ."

"Not dead!" exclaimed Canon Pethick, while Dannie and Slugger remained speechless.

"Hush! It seems he had a terrible wife. He's told me all about it often. The opportunity came in this unexpected way; he hadn't planned it. He escaped, slipped through the millet and made his way to the coast. He has never gone back. He's under an assumed name but of course I knew him instantly, poor old Harry, when he turned up looking for work."

Neither Dannie nor the Slugger needed to hear any more. Their minds had seized the same idea. "Excuse us a few minutes, father," Dannie said. And within a few minutes they were seated in Mr. Sheppardson's office. This time they held all the cards in the pack.

Mr. Sheppardson never doubted them. He knew a fact when he heard it. "Quite so, exactly so," he repeated, "oh, absolutely so." No question of any further discussion. Indeed," he said, "this puts a rather different face on every side of the matter, among other things on the whole question of Mrs. Fordeck's maintenance . . ."

"Hasn't she got—" Dannie began.

"Practically nothing. A small, a very small, annuity of her own, very small. She has no interest in the estates; they go to a cousin. And, of course, the property left by her late husband—I should say, by her present husband—is all gone long ago, the greater part of it, in fact, in legal expenses. You see, the property, such as it was, was in Ohio and we had the greatest fight to prove that Fordeck was dead, that is, dead in Ohio. Several times they brought him in alive on appeal while admitting that he might be dead in Africa or dead for the purposes of interstate commerce. The distinction was very interesting—and expensive," added Mr. Sheppardson, musingly.

"What did you do?" asked Dannie.

"We managed it at last through the kindness of the Governor of Bechuanaland, Sir Harry Hoppit, who happened to have financial connections through our firm; in fact we have advanced him funds. He got for us, by a legal fiction, the conviction of a native in a Magistrates' Court for the murder of Harry Fordeck. That, of course, settled the matter but it involved"—Mr. Sheppardson paused—"The native's family," he said, "were compensated."

"Then Mrs. Fordeck received the money?"

"And spent it."

Then they were all silent.

"Of course," said Mr. Sheppardson, "she will now have Fordeck. He has a certain earning power."

"That's right," they said.

"He's only sixty-six," said Mr. Sheppardson.

"That's all," they said.

And they all had the same vision of two drudging worn-out lives moving on to their end, hopeless.

Then messages began to run up and down the skeins of destiny all the way to ancient Syracuse.

Dannie spoke first.

"Look," he said, "I'm thinking of something," and Pethick said, "I know it—so am I."

"What I mean is this: She'd have got twenty thousand dollars anyway and instead of that she's going to be right up against it. I'm going to give it to her myself, not directly in my own name but through Mr. Sheppardson."

"Mr. Sheppardson rose and shook Dannie's hand; there were tears in his eyes.

"That's very noble," he said, "very noble. I shall be only too glad to arrange it."

"Wait a minute," said the Slugger. "Just hold on. You needn't do that, Dannie. You'll need all you've got to start your old man up again. I'll give it."

"This is touching—touching—" said Mr. Sheppardson; he saw business and his eyes grew moist.

"You need it, too, for yours," protested Dannie. "Don't be a chump."

Something like anger developed, till Dannie said, "What does it matter anyway, Peth? Why, Haddock Park—I mean Ohio Gardens—is worth ten times that all by itself. We'll both give it."

"Gentlemen, gentlemen," said Mr. Sheppardson with an uplifted hand, "this is indeed magnanimous. Let me write it down."

"All right," they said.

"I will see," said Mr. Sheppardson, "that she never knows where it came from. Indeed, I am only too glad to associate myself in any way as a third in such an enterprise . . ." (And the shade of the Tyrant of Syracuse heard him with approval.)

Dannie and Pethick left.

Mr. Sheppardson used to say afterwards that there were tears in his eyes, that he even thought, before he had had time to reflect, of charging no commission on the transaction.

But Dannie and Pethick had stepped out into a changed world—how bright it seemed, this glorious autumn day. And when they got back to their office the very joy of their faces brought a new cheeriness to the countenances of their fathers.

Charles Edward Dament sad?—broken?— Oh, no!—just a first impression. Nothing could break a man like that. Already he was recovering his old-time spirit with every moment.

"Watch me get busy sending out messages for that dinner," said Dannie, and he added, "Darned if I won't try the telephone. I believe it's quicker."

And in less than ten minutes he was actually talking to the caterer.

It was a memorable dinner—just as Dannie had planned and dreamed it—all except the cheques. There was no need for that as they all took the money for granted. And Dannie's father, back with the old crowd was his old self again—and so were the Canon and the Bishop and Colonel Strong, all their old selves, with old wine and old jokes, and old reminiscences and not a remark that hadn't at least twenty years retrospect behind it.

Mr. Sheppardson arrived later. He had been with Mrs. Fordeck. Everything was arranged. Mr. Sheppardson said that she had guessed his uneasy secret at once, her husband still alive and their generous provision. It had brought tears to her eyes.

"A wonderful woman," said Mr. Sheppardson, "such resilience. She's making plans already. She proposes to pick up Harry at once and start for Bechuanaland. I shall have to communicate with Sir Harry Hoppit." He added musingly, however, "We needn't trouble about that," and he fell to on the walnuts and the wine.

XV

BOOM TIMES

The Mirage of a Better World
A Word of Preface

SOME readers may be kind enough to recall a sketch which I published in a magazine two or three years ago called, *My Remarkable Uncle,* which afterward became the title piece of a book of sketches. I now take the same distinguished actual person and remove him from the cramped environment of truth to the larger atmosphere of fiction. After the opening page he parts company with his origin, and the people who surround him are, individually, fiction, although, I hope, living pictures of the time and place.

I have given to the story the sub-title *The Mirage of a Better World* for reasons made obvious in the text, but still more obvious if I mention them now. I have always been greatly impressed with the alternate sunshine and shadow that fall, or used to fall, in places newly opened, in the world that was, to which people flocked as to a promised land, as they did to the Manitoba of 1880. This promised land for the time being transformed them all into a life better than what we have, and into characters better and more distinctive than the everyday people about us but no better than the everyday people ought to be. The mirage of hope and the illusion of fancy faded out to give way to the sad reality of failure just as the fading mirage in the sky leaves, in the place of the vanished oasis, nothing but the waterless sand of the desert. Yet the real mirage over the desert is *true;* it is not a mere confusion of light and shadow that the eye of misery converts to a picture of hope. It is the reflection of an actuality of green trees and pleasant waters, miles and miles away —if you will—and even inverted in their outline in the sky— but none the less attainable for those who will walk bravely forward, animated by illusion itself.

It seems to me also that this alternation of sunshine and shadow, so plainly to be seen in the boom times and bad times of a new Eldorado, characterizes also all the economic side of our collective human life. We see it in the alternating prosperity and depression of big business of which the "peaks" and "crashes" of the stock exchange are only the outward signs of the tumult within, like the glow from the crater of a volcano that reveals the subterranean fires. Most of all does this appear in the strange and elusive war prosperity, the good times that by some devil's contrivance come with the onslaught of war to mock the failure of peace. In these things is to be sought, I believe, the solution of the unsolved problem of wealth and want. To me the boom is not the exception but the reality. It is a vision of what ought to be happening all the time. The boom in Winnipeg in 1880 ought to be booming still.

So, too, with the cheery good times of big business that come only to slip away again; and most of all with the war prosperity that chases away idleness and unemployment like shadows of the night and calls out the higher self of inspired people living among us unseen. In that sense each of us should be at war for ever.

All such things are better seen on a smaller scale than on a large. There is a deep meaning in these contrasts with the problem of poverty or prosperity after the war. To such people I especially try to appeal in this picture of *BOOM TIMES*.

WHEN Edward Philip Philiphaugh arrived from England at his brother's farm in a lost corner of Ontario in the late summer of 1878, he seemed, to the children of the family, like a wonderful being, dropped from the sky. The elder brother had settled there with his wife and children a few years earlier. He had left England first to settle in South Africa, and had been eaten out by locusts. He had then moved to Kansas but had been eaten out by grasshoppers. A grasshopper is a locust. On the Ontario farm there were no grasshoppers; only just mortgages and broken machinery and thin cattle.

The farm was thirty-five miles from a railway. They lived on it in an isolation unknown, in these days of radio, anywhere in the world. There were no newspapers. Nobody came and went. There was nowhere to come and go. In the solitude of dark winter nights the stillness was that of eternity.

Into this isolation broke Edward Philip. He had just come from a year's travel round the Mediterranean, a man of twenty-eight or thirty, but seeming a more than adult man, bronzed and self-confident, with a square beard like a Plantagenet king. He arrived in the dusk of a late summer evening in a two-horse wagon, filled with English leather portmanteaus and bundles of double-barreled guns, fishing rods and malacca canes—things that he called his "kit."

That night at supper the children listened wide-eyed to

"Uncle Edward," with visions of Algiers, of the African slave market, of the Golden Horn, and the Pyramids. Lizzie, the hired girl, stood open-mouthed, and when she heard him say, "So, I said to the Prince of Wales" . . . she dropped the plates with a crash . . . "Uncle Edward," said the children, "do you know the Prince of Wales?" He answered quite simply, "Oh, very well indeed," as if that was nothing.

"Uncle Edward," said the oldest boy, Jim, who was fifteen, "I'd like to be a soldier . . ." and his uncle said, "Then I must write to Lord Hartington at the War Office, and ask him to put you into Sandhurst . . ."

Now it happened that in that year, 1878, there was a general election in Canada. E.P.—as everybody began to call him—was in it up to the neck in less than no time. He picked up the history and politics of Upper Canada in a day, and in a week knew everybody in the countryside. He spoke at every meeting, but his strong point was the personal contact of electioneering, of bar-room treats. This gave full scope for his marvellous talent for flattery and make-believe.

"Why, let me see"—he would say to some tattered country specimen beside him glass in hand—"surely, if your name is Framley, you must be a relation of my dear friend General Sir Charles Framley of the Horse Artillery." "Mebbe," the flattered specimen would answer. "I guess, mebbe; I ain't kept track very good of my folks in the old country." "Dear me! I must tell Sir Charles that I've seen you. He'll be so pleased." In this way in a fortnight E.P. had conferred honours and distinctions on half the township of Georgina. They lived in a recaptured atmosphere of generals, admirals and earls. Vote? How else could they vote than conservative, men of family like them?

It goes without saying that in politics, then and always, E.P. was on the conservative, the aristocratic side, but along with that was hail-fellow-well-met with the humblest. This was instinct. A democrat can't condescend. He's down already. But when a conservative stoops, he conquers.

He was not only a conservative but an imperialist in a large way. He made full use, then and always, of the British Empire as if he had a share in all of it, and might at any time be leaving for any part of it.

"Are you likely to be long in Georgina Township?" an innocent questioner would ask.

"That will depend a good deal," he answered impressively, "on what I hear from West Africa." Most of them never heard anything from West Africa.

This made his presence in any one place a favour and a distinction.

But for his electioneering E.P. had not only his impressive line of talk but also a quite opposite way of telling Gargantuan stories that would make the country crowd in the bar roar and wheeze and slap their thighs, as for instance, when they heard the story of how the old Earl of Kinraith had called his wife an "auld Highland cow," and she had answered, "Aweel, it's better than an auld steer."

It was an old-fashioned election, all carried on in the open air in bright September weather with flags, placards and torchlight processions. The hustings were big wooden platforms, with a rail around. Committee men in plug hats sat on the platform. Farmers stood in a crowd in front—no women.

A liberal speaker spoke from a platform with banners all

around it—DESMOND AND LIBERTY—DOWN WITH THE TORY PARTY. "What has the Tory party ever done for this country?" he shouted, shaking his fist in the air. "Tramped it down, tramped down the plain people under foot . . . We never had a thing unless we wrested it from them . . . We've got them out of power. I say let's keep them out . . . They're against the people . . . my father and my uncle carried their muskets in the rebellion of forty years ago . . . I was fifteen . . . I wanted to go . . . They wouldn't let me . . . They went with the 'rebels . . .' That is what the Tories called them . . . 'rebels . . .' They went . . . and my uncle never came back . . . they hanged him there in front of the courthouse in Toronto . . . hanged him with the Tories to jibe and laugh, and a holiday for the school children to go and see a rebel hanged . . . that's Tories for you . . . let them into power again and that's what they would do again."

On the other hustings stood Edward Philip Philiphaugh, set and firm, the embodiment of resolution, his gaze direct in front of him. All about him were Union Jacks and banners with STRONG AND LOYALTY—and—GOD SAVE THE QUEEN.

His voice went clear over the heads of the crowd.

"You ask me what has the Tory party done for Canada? *There* is your answer in those waving flags whose crosses chronicle the union of the British people. There, in that loyalty that stands fast and firm against each and every phase of sedition. I will not talk in paltry figures of trade and taxes. I scorn them. I appeal here to all in whose veins run the blood, in whose hearts beat the life—of the mother country . . . I see here before me men whose names connect with some of the oldest families of Great Britain . . . my friend

Framley, a cousin, I believe, of Sir Charles Framley, one of England's greatest soldiers . . . Major Wyndham, a close relation, a possible successor to, the Earl of Egremont . . . my friend Donald McLeish who stands here as one of the McLeishes of McLeish . . . to shout *Scots wha' hae!*

(tumult—applause)

. . . "Here on my heart—," he drew out a photograph and held it up—"I carry—I always carry—a photograph of our beloved Queen. That is my politics, it is your politics, electors of North York."

(applause—tumult)

So there came an evening with the village all lit with torchlights, when a committee man stepped out before the Tory crowd in front of the Mansion House, and said:

"Gentlemen of North York, I beg to inform you that the official count of votes elects to Parliament at Ottawa, Dr. John Strong of Aurora by a majority of two thousand votes—gentlemen, *God Save the Queen!* They sang it from a thousand throats—"*Send . . . her . . . victorious . . . Happy . . . and . . . glorious!*"

A few nights after the election E.P. was summoned to a general meeting of the Conservative Committee of the Ridings of York County. The chairman spoke:

"Mr. Philiphaugh, I want to express to you on behalf of the Conservative party of the County of York an appreciation of your co-operation in the election of Dr. Strong . . .

" . . . Mr. Philiphaugh, we want to keep you here. I have heard some of our people saying that you think of moving on to Manitobah.* But I'm glad to say that we are here to give

---

* *So pronounced in 1880.*

ou an appointment that will keep you safe from going to
:arve among the grasshoppers!

(Laughter—"Ya, Ya! That's right!")

"Hitherto we've had no salaried organizer in the Ridings
f York County and the Association is prepared to offer you
uch a post and to offer it on terms that show we're in earnest
nd pay a man according to his real worth. Mr. Philiphaugh,
n behalf of these gentlemen of the Committee, I offer you a
ilary of $1,000 a year as organizer of the Conservative Party
1 York County."

(Applause—"Hurrah for E.P.!—Hurrah!")

"For he's a jolly good fellow!"

E.P. spoke:

"Gentlemen:—When I tell Sir John A. Macdonald, our
eader, of your generous offer, I am sure he will be as deeply
ouched as I am. And when I send word, as I hope you will
llow me to do, to Lord Beaconsfield, of the loyalty and alle-
iance of the County of York, I am sure that he will see fit to
lace your names before Her Majesty for such honour as she
nay see fit to bestow. But, gentlemen, for me, my lot is cast,
s you yourselves would say *Alea jacta est!* . . . *nulla ves-
igia retrorsum . . ."*

(Dubious voices—"Hear! Hear!")

'The Star of the Empire glitters in the West . . . I see in
Manitobah . . .

(voices—grasshoppers—grasshoppers)

"I see in Manitobah a great future. I look forward to the
ime when two million people will be settled on the western
rairies—"

(laughter—"They'll freeze—Ya—Ya")

—a great future—a great vision—it is my destiny to go."

(applause—handshaking—tumultuous talk.)

E.P. left next morning taking his nephew Jim with him as his private secretary. Jim couldn't even spell but that didn't matter; it was only to last till Lord Hartington was to give him a commission in the British Army.

To get to Winnipeg they went up the Lakes and across Minnesota. It was the only way then. They hit Winnipeg just on the rise of the boom, and E.P. came at once into his own and rode on the crest of the wave. There is something that appeals in the rush and movement of a "boom" town— a Winnipeg of the 80's, a Carson City of the 60's. Life comes to a focus; it is all here and now, all present, no past and no outside—just a clatter of hammers and saws, rounds of drinks and rolls of money. In such an atmosphere every man seems a remarkable fellow, a man of exception; individuality separates out and character blossoms like a rose. And before the eyes of each as he hammers, and works and talks, is the mirage of the wonder that is to come—the mirage of what might be—of what the world is meant to be—always coming, but it never comes.

E.P. came into his own. In less than no time he was in everything and knew everybody, conferring titles and honours up and down Portage Avenue.

His activities were wide. He was president of a bank (that never opened), head of a brewery (for brewing the Red River), and, above all, secretary-treasurer of the Winnipeg Arctic Ocean and Siberian Railway that had a charter authorizing it to build a road to the Arctic Ocean, when it got ready. They had no track, but they printed stationery and passes, and in return E.P. received passes over all North America.

He knew everybody, but in particular he gathered to himself, round the saloons, a particular set of adherents, men of that queer class that turns up in a place like the Winnipeg of 1880—dead broke, but gentlemen, and not worrying. There was Captain Desmond Despard. He had been at a "public" school, at it—and out of it. He had been "sent down" from Oxford, and "sent up" from Sandhurst. He used whiskey like milk. But he was a well-educated man; at any rate everybody in the bars agreed on that. "Nothing like education, Jim," he would say. "E.P. should send you home to a public school. Look at me; would I be where I've got to if I hadn't been at a public school?" And he would quote a line—the first line—of Virgil. It was the only line he knew but it had taken him half round the world.

Then there was little Count Fosdari—Count Fosco di Fosdari. As soon as E.P. knew he was a *real* count, one of the family of the Fosdaris of Fosforetto, he annexed him. Fosdari was "good medicine."

All these friends he put on the boards of his new companies. They were always in and out of his huge wooden office building, half finished—always half finished, because the minute it began to look finished he added more to it. Fosdari was a director of the Winnipeg Arctic Ocean and Siberian Railway with his name on the letter-head right under that of the Marquis of Madeira. Captain Despard was president of the brewery. Jim was private secretary to everything.

But naturally E.P.'s main hold was on politics. They elected him right away into the Manitoba Legislature. He made a speech on the hustings in which he said, "I will not talk in terms of paltry figures of trade and taxes. I scorn them." And he showed his photograph of the Queen. It made a great impression. He made the same speech in the

Manitoba Assembly. His public policy was for spending all the money they could get, on everything they could think of to spend it on. His specialty was vision—mirage. "I can foresee a time, Mr. Speaker, in no distant future, when there will be three million people on these western plains." He had started it at two, but moved it up. He wanted at once to float a huge loan in London, and sink it right there. There was talk after this of making him Prime Minister.

E.P. bought a huge house beside the river and filled it with pictures that he said were portraits of his ancestors. One of them, such a fine old portrait that it was nothing but black soot round a dark face, E.P. said was the Marquis of Madeira, the founder of his family. In this great house he instituted a roaring hospitality that never stopped. In it was installed a heavy English butler, Meadows, with a British army medal. "A Crimean veteran," E.P. explained. He wasn't really a veteran, because he hadn't been in the army, and E.P. had bought the medal in a second-hand shop, and his name wasn't Meadows. But that didn't matter; it was not a matter of what was but of what should have been. It was a sort of mirage of an "interior."

Then there was Harris, the footman, a young man chosen for his gentlemanly voice and extraordinary manners. As Harris went out with a tray, E.P. would whisper behind his hand to his guests, "An illegitimate son of the Prince of Wales." Harris's mother hadn't known this. But any one could see that if the Prince of Wales had had an illegitimate son, Harris would be just the kind of illegitimate son the Prince of Wales would have wished to have.

There was a huge cook "Jennings"; not Mrs. Jennings or Jessie Jennings but just "Jennings." And housemaids called

by their surnames—Parker and Anderson. It made a great hit
with plain people not used to it, to hear E.P. say, "Anderson,
kindly tell Parker—" and so on. Their names weren't really
that. Parker had been Dulcie McGinnis and Anderson had
been Phoebe McLean.

The house was run, as E.P. said, *on system*. Jennings
brought her book to E.P. and E.P. gave it to Jim. And Jim
gave it back to Jennings. Anyway it didn't matter what
things cost.

Everything was done on that sort of scale, more and more.
Presently even the ancestors weren't good enough. E.P. invented a Portuguese dukedom and conferred it, by a sort of
reversion, on Jim, as of the senior branch of the family,
ahead of himself, an affectation of inferiority known only to
nobility.

To visitors he would show them round the ancestors.

"Strange to think that two deaths would make that boy a
Portuguese duke!"

E.P. met Agnes Dacres,—the Honorable Mrs. De Carteret
Dacres—at one of those huge fashionable receptions that had
become the fashion, quite the rage, that is to say, the fashion
to be fashionable, in the Winnipeg of the Boom. The mirage
that coloured all the world of business and money was ex-
tending to the world of social life. Everybody suddenly
became of high family, of high official position, or closely
related to some one of high family or of high official position.
So at such receptions people crushed round drinking cups of
tea standing up, and drinking champagne and rye whiskey
leaning beside sideboards and introducing first cousins of
earls to sister of bishops. "Mrs. McGruder, do let me introduce the Hon. Charles Dewdrop; Captain Dewdrop, **you**

know, is one of the Dewdrops of Devonshire. Your father, of course, was Major General McGruder of Mississippi, wasn't he? Your cousin? Oh, yes, your cousin" . . . a niece of the Earl of Gallaway; oh . . . how do you do?"

And they didn't say it in stage whispers—not a bit—they bandied it all round quite openly—Dukes, Generals, Ministers of the Crown—the whole place was a galaxy—and everybody willing to believe it—and everybody so happy in it. Here was a new social world all made of mirage, of the colours of the rainbow—as easy as that. And with it all, was a closer reach towards truth than the ordinary drab of social life. Give and take and you've got everything.

In such a social world E.P. came into his own. At the receptions he was always to be seen at a sideboard, the men packed around him, listening to one of his Gargantuan stories, and the ladies all dying to catch what he was saying. E.P. would stand against the bar saying: "Well, there we were at Algiers, all standing round at the big reception, a *divan,* given by the Dey of Algiers to the Navy. There was the Dey, all in uniform, a tremendously fat fellow, stomach like this —diplomats and officers—that sort of thing. Well, in came old Admiral Mannering—I mean to say, simply spiflicated!—and the Vizier said, 'Let me present you to the Dey.' And the Admiral said, 'Day? day! By gad, he looks like nine months!' "
(roars of laughter)

"Ya! ha! ya! ha!" and the story went all over Winnipeg.

It was at such a reception that somebody (either Colonel the Honorable Osborne Thisthewaite, or Señor Desdichado, the Consul-General for Mexico—anyway, somebody) dragged E.P. through the crowded reception given by Mrs. Pleasington, a niece of the Governor of Bombay, and said, "Do let me introduce you to Mrs. Dacres, a cousin of the Duke of Somerset." E.P., with a bow of deference fit for Versailles, said, "I'm *so* glad to meet you. I used to know your cousin, the Duke of Somerset so well." And she said, "Oh, how delightful. Do you know I haven't heard a word from any of the Somersets for weeks and weeks." Neither she had. So they moved together to drink champagne at a sideboard, caught up in the mirage of make-believe as superior to truth, as fireflies are to gas light.

Mrs. Dacres had arrived in Winnipeg a little before, and was living in shabby lodgings—the Honorable Mrs. De Carteret Dacres—with her little daughter Evelyn. Evelyn was fourteen and Mrs. Dacres was—well, the very least you can be if you have a daughter of fourteen. Mrs. Dacres was as impecunious as she was pretty and as charming as she was both. And she had the same mirage of family and money as Edward Philiphaugh, and when she talked her talk was based on the peerage. She was "honorable" because she said she was honorable. People let it go at that. Her husband had died in India and when she spoke of India she spoke of "cantonments" and "syces" and Simla and of how India was such a small place that of course everybody knew everybody. She left out the other three hundred million. So people thought her husband had been in the army. But in reality he had been with an export tea firm in Calcutta. Sometimes she shifted him to the Zulu war because that was recent. Her talk was so vague that you could never quite locate him. Some people understood that he had got the Victoria Cross in Afghanistan—Winnipeg was full of Victoria Crosses in 1880. Mrs. Dacres never *said* these things. But they came out somehow in conversation with her over the teacups. If people believed them then she couldn't help it. And in reality she faced and fought poverty with the bravery of a heroine.

Now the truth was that Mrs. Dacres' late husband far from being rich had been poor, and worse. For he had put all his money and his savings into the Gujahar Swindle that is still remembered in odd corners of England. This was when a company was floated by the Majarajah of Gujahar to grow tea. The British Government was to—should have, was certain to—back the enterprise. It didn't. No tea was grown and the Gujahar loan went the way of Turkish bonds. Dacres of Calcutta had put in all his money. He had done more. He had put in, without her knowledge, all his wife's money, the little bit of money that every girl in England of that kind and class used to have. That was how he came to die. He died—they found him dead—the evening the news came out. Mrs. Dacres never spoke of it; and in any case the worst of it, the last part, they never told her. She thought it was apoplexy. But perhaps she knew. That was why, in Winnipeg, she never mentioned Gujahar.

Her little girl, Evelyn—she liked to call her "my baby"—was, as said, fourteen years old, but Mrs. Dacres got her down to twelve in general conversation. Evelyn was just as pretty as her mother, and as fickle as a summer breeze. She couldn't help it, because she just had to be whatever you wanted her to be. If a curate talked to her of the love of God, she looked as sad as a saint, because she felt like a saint. But if you wanted her to be a kitten she'd turn into one.

"So Lord Decimer came over,' Mrs. Dacres was saying to Evelyn, "and patted you on the head . . ." She was speaking in their shabby sitting room, knitting with some wool which, as her friends understood, the Duchess of Bedford had sent her. She only knitted things not to disappoint the Duchess. She knitted and as in a mirage, she was saying, "So Lord Decimer . . ."

"Mother," said Evelyn, "did we *really* know all those people in India?"

"Who, dear?"

"Lord Decimer and the Prince of Wales and . . ."

"My dear child! What a question! Why you must remember yourself how I took you into the House of Lords—no, let me see; perhaps you don't. You were only three. But, my dear Evelyn, when you ran into the Prince with your hoop and he was so . . ."

"But, mother, I don't remember any of it."

"No, perhaps not. Let me see; you were only two."

"But, mother, at two? I couldn't have run a hoop at two."

The bell rang from below and Evelyn went down and back. "It's the grocery man, mother, he's brought back the cheque you gave him yesterday. He said the bank wouldn't take it." Mrs. Dacres looked at the cheque.

"How silly of me! I'm always doing that . . ."

She went over to a desk and took out about eight blank cheque books, thought a little and selected one and wrote a new cheque.

"There, tell him I'm so sorry—I'd written it on the wrong bank . . ."

"But, mother," persisted Evelyn when she came back, "I don't remember living in those big houses in England. I only remember such a little house in a village."

"But of course, dear . . . I *adore* little houses—so simple. Look at *this*. They never could get me to London. I remember the dear old Count Chateau de Chateaubriand saying,

'*Mais, pourquoi,* madame' . . . perfect French . . . just like that '*pourquoi,* madame' . . ." Another tradesman's cheque came up. Mrs. Dacres made apologies again. It was so stupid of her. She had written 1890 instead of 1880. People who wait and wait for remittances from home do these things. "But stop," said Mrs. Dacres, "it must be dinner time—" she looked at her watch and murmured, "That tiresome jeweler . . . Yes, it must be dinner time. You're having dinner at the Smith's, aren't you? No, dear, I shan't have any. I'm not a bit hungry!"

So when the Honorable Mrs. Dacres went out to tea all her friends talked about Philip Philiphaugh and she thought him wonderful.

She bought a newspaper every day just to see what it said about him. A newspaper in Winnipeg cost ten cents.

So one day the Honorable Mrs. Dacres found herself in Philip Philiphaugh's combined offices that carried on their front in gigantic letters the sign boards of the Saskatchewan, Manitoba Real Estate Company—The Peace River Development Company, and the Winnipeg Arctic Ocean and Siberian Railway. All these enterprises were at their height, with outer offices and inner offices going full swing, with every luxury in furniture and fittings that the Winnipeg of 1880 could contrive, and with Count Fosco di Fosdari, speaking Italian in all of them, and with doorkeepers to show people in and out, all English army veterans with one leg each.

Charmingly Mrs. Dacres bent over the counter and extended her card: *The Honorable Mrs. Dacres.* It worked as magic. The great man appeared in a moment. "Do please come in, Mrs. Dacres—do take a chair. You must excuse a

rather ramshackle office; our mahogany furniture is all de-
layed at sea. Lord Beresford cabled that he can do simply
nothing about it."

"My little girl, Evelyn," murmured Mrs. Dacres. "I like to
call her my baby still, but she is really eleven." "Oh, charming!" exclaimed Philiphaugh, "but dear me, who is it she
reminds me of—why, of course, the little Princess of Saxe-
Schlitz-in-Main." "Why, she *is* like her, and yet I never noticed it before," echoed Mrs. Dacres. "Do let me call Count
Fosdari," went on Edward Philip. Then, opening the door,
he called, *"Fate venire, si piace, il Conte Fosdari"*—which
was good medicine for the outer office.

E.P. took for granted that the Hon. Mrs. Dacres wanted to
invest. He showed her on the wall a huge map of the Peace
River country. It seemed that Lord Salisbury had cabled
over for half of it. But some was left; also a good deal of the
Arctic and all Siberia. A mirage seemed to colour the room
as he spoke.

Mrs. Dacres took out a cheque book—one on London—she
had another with her on Bombay. Evelyn looked at her, a
straight direct look, and she felt guilty. She wondered—
nearly broke off—and then the mirage grew rosier still when
Philip Philiphaugh said, "Oh, please don't bother with a
cheque. We'll just call it an open account. Your profits will
pay it off in no time. But don't you think after all, a thousand pounds is too small—just a bagatelle. Suppose we say
fifty thousand dollars . . . and if you wish to draw out some
money in advance of profit, the Count (here the Count
bowed double, twice) will arrange at once . . ." And with
that E.P. threw a little more Italian at the Count.

E.P. showed Mrs. Dacres through the offices with great
dignity, Count Fosdari lingering behind with Evelyn. He

had made a bee-line to her at once, and was showing her a picture of his father's castle, and chattering Italian.

The Honorable Mrs. Dacres walked home, still in her mirage, with a thousand other mirages walking the Winnipeg streets, and greeting one another as they passed.

And Philiphaugh? Why had he done it? Why does any person do it? Why does a boy show off before a girl?

Mrs. Dacres spent that afternoon buying furs on Portage Avenue. Till now she had said she thought them vulgar.

But other banking transactions were going on that day in Winnipeg of a very different kind. In the private room in one of the *real* banks, one with a head office in Montreal, the manager talked with the manager of another real bank with a head office in Toronto. They had papers and books in front of them.

"It isn't banking!" he said. "Man, man, look at these accounts! Here's a loan company. What are their assets? Loans to a real estate company. What are their assets? Shares in the loan company. Here's another real estate company? Where does it get its funds? From the Brewery that bought the real estate. Look at this—Winnipeg Arctic and Siberian Railway."

"Donald," said the other, "you lent them fifty thousand . . ."

"Man, can I help it? If I didn't lend it you would . . . and I admit that darned man has a way with him. In he comes here and he starts talking about the Monteiths of Caithness—you'll understand—and knowing more about our tartan than I do myself. He's joined the Curling Club it seems, and wants a family tartan; he says he can buy one on a Royal Warrant . . ."

"That's it, Donald," said the other. "He can buy it with your fifty thousand."

So they both laughed, and agreed that it couldn't go on, that it must burst, and went away to blow it up all the harder . . .

When Evelyn and her mother got home Mrs. Dacres seemed very thoughtful. But Evelyn danced all round the room. *"Tra-la-la!*⁻ . . . Is an Italian count's wife called— what?" "Mother, where is Lake Como?. . . *Tra-la-la!*"

So the autumn waned and the winter came. The river froze and the prairie was a white sheet of frozen snow but the rush of business never slackened and the pace and throb of life were as warm as ever. So it came about that one winter day E.P. took Mrs. Dacres out driving, in a two-seated cutter, drawn by two horses dancing under tall sleighbells. They skimmed over the prairie like the wind. You drove any-where over the prairie then, just right over the prairie, as soon as you left the town. E.P. and Mrs. Dacres were in front and Evelyn and Jim behind, the big cutter smothered over with buffalo robes and Arctic furs, and Mrs. Dacres and Evelyn with "clouds" over their faces against the cut of the wind. These "clouds" of 1880 were loose-knitted woolen things of bright pink and lighter blue, guaranteed dangerous at ten yards. On the front seat E.P. was explaining to Mrs. Dacres that two deaths might at any time make Jim a Portu-guese Duke. Evelyn nudged Jim and Jim nudged Evelyn and Jim whispered, "Which two do I kill?" because each of them had been brought up alongside mirage and humbug, and each knew that the other knew all about it.

Such drives were a great success. E.P. used to help Mrs. Dacre into the sleigh with a courteous, "Allow me, Agnes," and help her out again—"Allow me, Agnes—" with a chivalry of voice and manner worthy of the Middle Ages.

Then in less than no time it was summer again, for there is no spring in the west, and E.P. took them out in his big sail-boat on the Red River . . . (people could still sail on it then). It was quite a large picnic party and E.P. told them about yachting off the Isle of Wight with the Prince of Wales, and how one day in a sudden storm the Prince called, "Ned, for God's sake take the helm!"

After that Agnes called him "Ned," a name just for herself to use. Count Fosdari, who was one of the party that day, made a great hit by talking heroically about Christopher Columbus, till he fell over the gunwale into the water. After which he had to go home and was out of the picnic, a marvelous picnic on the river bank with such a clatter of plates and knives, with salads and cold pâtés and champagne popping and everybody talking at once. "I remember saying to the Dey of Algiers . . ." Now, then, Agnes, allow me . . . "I remember . . ."

The strange thing was that when Agnes Dacres was with E.P. all the "pretense" seemed to drop away from her. She let him tell her about the Portuguese title in his family. She never spoke of one in hers.

In fact, quite the contrary. Evelyn noticed it right away. After they had come home from such an outing, her mother would say:

"Evelyn, you've always thought the Duke of Somerset is my cousin. Well, he isn't."

And Evelyn answered, "I knew he wasn't, mother."

And another day:

"Evelyn you've always thought that that photograph is a picture of my house when I was a child. Well, it isn't. My father was a country curate with six children, and I went out to Calcutta as a governess."

And once, a little later and with much greater difficulty, she said:

"Evelyn, when we were in India—you've always thought your father was in the army. Well—he wasn't."

She was speaking hesitantly, with pauses, as she sat "fixing her face" before a glass. It was easier to say things when she was doing something.

"He was in a tea house in Calcutta," she went on, "and we didn't know anybody. I never saw Simla, dear."

" . . . Oh, mother, I'm so sorry."

" . . . And we were very poor . . . and then all that your father could save in ten years, and the little money I had, he put into the terrible Gujahar Swindle . . . and it was all lost."

"The what? Mother, what a funny word . . ."

"Gujahar! It's a native state in India . . . the Gujahar Swindle . . . everybody knows about it. The Maharajah—think of the wickedness of it—organized a great tea company —just on nothing, Evelyn; all on paper."

"But, mother, surely in Winnipeg they do that every day?"

"But this is Winnipeg; that was Gujahar."

"But, mother, a company like the Winnipeg Arctic and Siberian Railway—Jim says that his uncle and the rest never put a cent into it; his uncle said that himself."

"Eveyln, that's an utterly different thing. Didn't you hear him say that if he could get a million pounds from England, he would sink it all in the Arctic Ocean? But Gujahar was a *swindle*. The Maharajah got it all; the rest were ruined; it killed your father."

Then there came an evening, an unforgettable evening, of an old-fashioned party in E.P.'s spacious house with Agnes Dacres acting as hostess to his guests. They had all the old-fashioned items and features of the day, little tables of whist, and people singing drawing-room pieces at the piano as they used to sixty years ago.

Captain Despard sang in a bold defiant voice: *" 'Tis a rich—rough—gem—Deny—it—who—can—'Tis the Island—Home—of—an Englishman."*

And E.P. turned the music while Agnes sang, *"In—the—gloaming—Oh, my darling!"*—and all the people listened, yearning, as people could yearn before moving pictures over-strained their capacity for it.

As E.P. showed Mrs. Dacres into the carriage which he had ordered to take her home, he held her hand a moment, under the summer leaves and said, in such a wonderful tone: "Agnes, dear—let this be our gloaming now . . ."

No one was surprised when the wedding was announced; nor at the stir it made, nor at the tremendous receptions that followed it, in E.P.'s great house.

His wife stood with a fan, like a princess, on a hearth rug and E.P. presented his political constituents and supporters, finding a title and an office for each.

"Agnes, dear, let me present the Reeve of Kildonan—

he ex-warden of Stony Mountain—the Assessor of Proven-
cher . . ."

E.P. could find a title for anybody that sounded like a
Walter Scott novel.

In the new social life that followed, with pretty clothes to
wear, Evelyn blossomed as quickly as a prairie rose, especially
as her mother now let her wear grown-up dresses. At the
receptions she made a wonderful hit with everybody. She let
the young and Reverend Fergus MacTavish, just ordained,
just arrived in Winnipeg, and nervous, tell her about damna-
tion—"But is *everybody* really damned, Mr. MacTavish?"
. . "I wouldna' just say everybody . . ." And she let a
young engineer, who had actually seen it, tell her how electric
light worked. "But what is it *really?*" she asked. While he
was telling her, she saw all sorts of things out of the corner of
her eye. "Do go on," she said, when he stopped. There was
more she wanted to see.

They had just time to enter on this grandeur, for what are
a few weeks and months when life moves as swiftly as happily
as that?—when down it all came with a crash. The great Manitoba boom broke—so suddenly and so completely that only
those who remember it can believe how suddenly and completely it broke.

It was all over, so to speak, in a day.

The headshaking and the whispering in the banks reached
its climax; the banks acted; they pulled out the planks of
credit, down came the house of faith. They drew the curtain
and the beautiful mirage was gone.

The hammers fell dead. The sounds ceased. All the new

world that was just going to be, and that might have been, broke into the wreckage of the world that is.

It was not only the loss of money. The change came with a sudden personal wrench to each and everyone. It was like the loss of a sudden glory, all this new wealth of character and personality, that had bloomed like a rose, this easy intercourse, this universal generosity and good fellowship, this marvellous mirage more true than reality. Hold it!—Stop it! —We can't let it go!

That's how the people felt, trudging the wooden sidewalks, looking for jobs.

In a moment everybody was bankrupt, everybody owed everybody. They always had, but it didn't matter then because nobody paid anybody. With the crash everybody called for pay.

Real estate went under. During the big boom people had bought land all night under the glare of torch- and lamp-light. Now they sold it all day in the cold daylight. The banks (the private banks) broke. The breweries burst. The insurance companies went up. The trust companies went under. The plain people could not bear to see it taken from them, this bright new world that was just beginning. Some tried to protest, little angry groups of men on street corners, with the snow blowing round them, for winter was come now. One was speaking from a box: "It isn't right! They've no right to close down on us. You know and I know, there's room here for thousands and thousands. You know and I know, it's just a crowd of rich men that are scared about their money."

Then two burly policemen with the real London manner would say, "Now then, move on, please, move on."

Who can agitate in a snowstorm?

And E.P.? Did he go under? Not for five minutes. What was a little thing like a crash to him. Of course he was ruined on such a huge scale that it made no difference and that it carried itself, as it were.

He explained it all away.

"It will be a matter of course of refinancing everything." He had a lot of words like that. "I shall cable to Lombard Street about 'converting' everything. The only trouble is that I may at any time now be needed in the Soudan."

So what with that and an unabated hospitality E.P. floated or seemed to, where others sank.

But not really. There was no reality underneath it. The big stuff was all over; what was left was just wreckage. After a few months ready money was clear gone. E.P. had to carry himself, when the company finances were broken, with personal loans at the banks.

Here he developed a wonderful technique. A banker, especially the manager of a branch, was E.P.'s natural mark and victim. He would tremble as E.P. came in, like a dove that sees a hawk. The method used by E.P. was so simple. It was like showing a farmer peas under a thimble. As he entered the banker's private office he would exclaim, "I say! Do you fish? Surely that's a green-heart casting-rod on the wall?" E.P. knew the names of everything. In a few minutes the banker, flushed and pleased, was exhibiting the rod, and showing flies out of a box in a drawer. When E.P. went out he carried a hundred dollars with him. There was no security. The transaction was all over.

But such sums, of course, were quite hopeless to maintain, not only E.P. but his establishment. Of course, there was still credit. E.P. would buy with that, though Agnes wouldn't. "I can't bear debt," she said. But E.P. would walk into shops as grandly as ever, buy with lavish generosity, never asking the price and never mentioning pay, until the parcel was in his hand and then: "By the way, please let me have the account promptly. I may be leaving very shortly for the Soudan . . ."

Sometimes it was the Soudan, sometimes Sir Henry Loch in West Africa, whichever was most in the papers.

Of course, E.P. could still travel. As a matter of fact he always carried with him the Charter of the Winnipeg Arctic Ocean and Siberian Railway, an impressive parchment with a big red seal. He could travel, which he did, in a sort of circuit, so as to be always "called east," or "called back west."

The hotels, of course, were easy. E.P. would always wait till he was all ready—coat, bag and all—and then ask for his bill at the desk, and receiving it, would break out with enthusiasm over the reasonableness of it. "But just compare that," he would say, "with the Hotel Crillon at Paris!" The manager couldn't; he just felt that he ran a cheap hotel. E.P. would add, "When I see Sir John I really must tell him how admirably I have been treated; he's coming here next week." Sir John was the Prime Minister. The hotel keeper hadn't known that he was coming; and he wasn't. Then came the final touch, "Let me see—seventy-six dollars—seventy-six—you give me"—and E.P. fixed his eye firmly on the hotel man—"give me twenty-four dollars and then I can remember to send an even hundred." The man's hand trembled. But he gave it.

Of course, it couldn't last. Credit faded month by month . . . There was no way to meet things up at the big house.

"You've let Meadows go?" asked a guest who missed the familiar butler and saw E.P. pour the whiskey himself.

E.P. shook his head very sadly, as if with great commisera-
tion.

"I had to," he said. "Poor chap! Drinking . . . but what
could I do?"

"Where's Harris?" asked another guest. "Has he left you?"
"Oh, no, only for a time. I've lent him to Government
House. Sir James and Lady Aikins were in despair. Of
course, I pay his wages."

"Is your wife out?" asked an evening visitor, who had been
invited to supper. "I'm so sorry she is," said E.P. "She told
me to tell you how terribly sorry she was not to see you . . .
She was called out."

Agnes wasn't out. She was in the kitchen down below,
getting supper ready to send up on the dumb-waiter, because
Anderson and Parker and Jennings were all gone. Agnes and
Evelyn did the work now.

At other times they tried other methods. At makeshift
dinner parties, for new people, Evelyn was turned into a
parlour maid. One English visitor, when she took his hat and
coat, gave her half a crown. E.P. sent her down the street
with it to the grocer's for a bottle of California wine, and
then served the wine, or had Evelyn serve it, to the visitor.
"Annette," he said, "bring up from the cellar a bottle of the
South African wine," and he added, "Cecil Rhodes has just
sent it. It is not half bad." Neither it was; or only half.

Evelyn made such a hit with herself as Annette that she
was in and out of character at two minutes notice.
Evelyn was also learning shorthand, and the new art—

type-writing—not proper work, of course, for a lady. The Legislature had taken over Jim to a job of selling law stamps in the courthouse. E.P. had lost his seat in the new elections, but they let Jim keep his job. Lord Hartington had never come across with the commission in the British Army; all the soldiering Jim got was training one night a week, in the long summer twilight, with the Winnipeg Field Battery—militia.

All that went on till months drifted into years. Then came a ray of hope; there might be some money for Agnes in England. Her father's estate was being wound up. He'd been dead for years but they were still winding. Her sister's husband, the Vicar of Little Bosing-on-the-Edge, Edgewater, near Exeter, England, had sent Agnes twenty pounds, taken out of the estate, to let her come home and help wind it. It seemed that there were some things that could only be arranged by agreement among the heirs.

Twenty pounds wasn't really enough; at least it meant going second class, and few people liked to admit doing that in 1884. So when they asked E.P., "What boat is your wife sailing on?" he said, "It's rather uncertain. She may take a Mediterranean boat out of New York." He might as well have said a banana boat out of Galveston, Texas, for all truth in it; but at least it stalled the question.

So Agnes went away, and E.P. shuffled along as best he could, a little shabbier all the time. Travel had broken down. The railways had cut out the Arctic Ocean since E.P. could print no more passes. Even the bar-rooms were breaking under him. There came a time when bar-room credit, the last refuge of human brotherhood, broke. E.P. had trailed into a bar with three adherents in tow. "Now, then," he said, in his grand manner, "what will you fellows have?" Then he held up his extended fingers to the bar man, and said, "Four." The head bartender looked round from mixing a fancy drink at a sideboard and broke into oaths. E.P. hooked Captain Despard by the arm. "Come away," he said. "I'm afraid the poor fellow's crazy; but I hate to report him."

Then Agnes wrote that she could not come back yet. The estate didn't seem to wind. Charles (that was the Vicar; he had taken a double blue and pink at Cambridge but all the business he knew was what he had learned out of Horace)— Charles said that there might in the end be quite a bit of money, but there wasn't any yet; in fact not even enough to come home with—and Charles himself had none.

So that was that, till the year 1884 ran out, and 1885 began with E.P. still talking of being called away—only now it was to Johannesburg. Evelyn was typing in a government office, and wishing that life would bring some romance to her life and none ever came. Jim selling law stamps and wishing he could be a soldier, and never a word from Lord Hartington. Jim and Evelyn had become in a sense "sweethearts" but not sweet enough for Evelyn. It was understood somehow that some day they were going to marry one another. But there was not enough *to it*. As Evelyn understood it, Jim was supposed to be waiting for "her answer." But he kept forgetting that he hadn't got it. It didn't seem possible to get up a real lovers' quarrel with Jim or to have final partings, or any of that sort of thing which makes love worth while.

Even the attentions of Count Fosdari, which Evelyn wished to apply as a torment, took no effect on Jim. He had a hereditary view of foreigners as silly asses. "I am sure that Count Fosdari would have proposed to me last night," Evelyn said.

"I just rushed out of the room in time." Or, "I wonder what Count Fosdari meant when he asked me if I thought I could live where it was always summer time?" "You can search me," said Jim, who was mending a fishing rod. "Some silly ass stuff about myrtle trees. He's nuts on them."

Then came the terrible blow to Evelyn when it turned out that Count Fosdari couldn't propose to her because he was married already. He had mentioned it quite innocently. He had a wife in Italy. She was twelve years old and in a convent. "Can you beat it?" Jim said. Fosdari must have meant engaged, Jim thought, but Evelyn said, "No, married."

It appeared that all of Fosdari's attentions had just been Italian antics. So Evelyn was left with less romance than ever, and Jim with no soldiering at all, unless you count the Field Battery, one evening a week.

Then fate pressed a button and gave him, and everyone else in Winnipeg, all the soldiering they wanted, and to Evelyn all the romance she could sustain.

There was plenty of forewarning, for those who could read the signs in the sky, of the oncoming of the rebellion of the halfbreeds and the Indians of the Northwest in the early spring of 1885. Yet few read or heeded them. When the rebellion broke it came with the sudden fury of a March blizzard. The attack on a column of mounted police by Gabriel Dumont's two hundred halfbreeds at Duck Lake, the heavy loss of life, the police driven back to their barracks—this news fell on Winnipeg with the sudden shock of impending danger. It even echoed across the ocean and around the Empire —the old days of savage warfare come back again.

All the more so when the news followed that the Crees of the Upper Saskatchewan had risen under Big Bear, had massacred people at Frog Lake, carried off the women captive, and were now moving to close in on Fort Pitt and Battleford, the little outlying posts in what was still almost empty country. There seemed no limit to what it all might mean . . . There were ten thousand halfbreeds on the lower Saskatchewan and twenty thousand Crees and Blackfoot Indians beyond. There were twenty thousand more beyond that. In Winnipeg, there were no permanent "soldiers," only volunteers, militia who drilled on summer evenings. These were the cavalry with sixty-two men (mostly on livery stable horses), the 90th. and 91st. battalions of the militia with about five hundred men and three hundred uniforms among them, and the Winnipeg Field Battery, sixty-two men with six guns, drilled and trained, the only effective unit west of Lake Superior. If the Indians really rose—all of them—then the country was all theirs till help could come. The rest of Canada was still cut off. The Canadian Pacific Railway was still one hundred miles short of completion; and the missing one hundred miles were in the frozen wilderness north of Lake Superior.

No wonder Winnipeg thrilled with excitement. The news from the plains came in as best it could by telegraph from here, there or anywhere, as riders might reach the railway telegraph station. It was written up on Bulletin Boards outside the newspaper offices, and sent out in "special editions" on broad sheets, like snow flakes . . . There were no telephones. The streets were full of people all day.

FORT PITT ABANDONED

POUNDMAKER TAKES WAR PATH

INSPECTOR DICKENS DEFENDS BATTLEFORD

And from the East:

TROOPS GATHERING AT TORONTO
TWENTY THOUSAND PEOPLE THRONG UNION STATION—ROYAL
GRENADIERS AND QUEEN'S OWN RIFLES ENTRAIN FOR WINNIPEG;
TROOPS REACH LAKE SUPERIOR GAP—SNOW BLIZZARD HALTS
MARCH.

And so on, endlessly. Jim was out of law stamps and into Artillery uniform and forage cap. The Battery was ready to go—and the 90th. and the 91st.—only waiting for the troops from Toronto. Meantime, regiments of "home guards" were being sworn in to defend the city.

E.P., standing beside the notice boards and in the bars said, "I shall take out a commission at once." Then it turned out they wouldn't give him one. After all, he'd never been in the army. "I shall simply cable to Lord Hartington at the War Office . . ." he said. He wrote a long cable at the telegraph office, marked it "collect," London, H.M.S. The clerk counted the words with his pencil—sixty words, he said "at forty-five cents a word, but it can't go collect." "That's all right," E.P. said, "but wait a minute. I think I must add something, it's hardly long enough—or, let me see . . . I think perhaps I'd better show it at Headquarters." So the cable didn't go. E.P. went round saying, "I'm in touch with Lord Hartington about a commission but Lord Hartington didn't know he was touched.

Then E.P. got a great idea.

"Desmond," he said, to Captain Despard, "I shall raise a Troop of Irregular Horse—I shall give you a commission." Despard hadn't taken out a commission, though he was a soldier, because just then he was taking in whiskey. Everybody was standing treat to ex-officers in Winnipeg just then. It was too good to lose. "Yes," said E.P., "a troop of horse— let me see, Fosdari's a soldier. I'll make him a lieutenant."

Those who recall the Northwest Rebellion will remember the little troops of horse that sprang into being at once, in every settlement in the Northwest, Boulton's Scouts, Steele's Scouts, the Alberta Rangers, the Surveyors' Intelligence Corps, all sorts—some with uniforms, most without, and with their own rifles or shotguns.

The idea no sooner struck E. P. than he saw the beauty of it . . . "Will you be going out against the rebels, Mr. Philiphaugh . . ." "I'm raising a troop of horse!" he said, returning his face to his glass . . . "I've just cabled White-hall for authorization." The word went round—"He's raising 'a troop of horse."

E.P. christened his troop, at birth, or before it, the Queen's Royal Intelligence. But in spite of its name there was no rush to join; particularly as it appeared that the troopers would get no pay.

So E.P. said it was just to be formed as a "skeleton corps." He himself was Major and Despard, Captain, and Fosdari a Lieutenant. E.P. dug up Meadows and called him a "trooper" and Harris and called him a "despatch rider." They had no uniforms but they had a lot of medals, Mead-ows' and two real ones of Despard's and some more that E.P. bought. They borrowed horses for each "parade" from a liv-ery stable. For all that, the Queen's Skeleton Intelligence was no less or worse than many other corps, especially after E. P. found a tailor with an unsaleable roll of butternut cloth and ordered what he called "service uniforms." That was, though they didn't know it, the beginning of khaki.

At this juncture arrived General Sir Frederick Middleton to command the column—all cocked hat and feathers and grey moustache and a red coat—the real thing. He was so completely muddled among men without uniform that the Queen's Intelligence got by—got on the books. This was partly because when Captain Despard saluted General Middleton, he did it with such an exact cavalry click to it that General Middleton said, "Where were you, sir?" Despard said, "Moari and Ashanti, sir." To the men standing round it sounded like a couple of Freemasons talking. "Come and have a peg," said the general, and that was that. All this time the messages kept coming in, brought to points on the railway from places on the plains that appeared as headlines.

"CREES RISING UNDER POUNDMAKER . . . SIOUX JOIN BIG BEAR . . . HALFBREEDS TAKE PRINCE ALBERT . . . LOUIS RIEL ON THE SOUTH SASKATCHEWAN . . . RUMOUR OF NEW MASSACRE AT FORT PITT.

"We can't wait," said General Middleton. He spoke on parade. "Men, our column must start now, without waiting for the rest. We must strike fast and while we can or we'll have all the Northwest on our hands."

So the Winnipeg column left—packed into box cars, coaches, cabooses, cattlecars, anything, with the field battery guns hauled up on box cars, with a great crowd of people at the station, so great that as the cars pulled out, Jim could hardly see which hat was Evelyn's and Evelyn could hardly see which forage cap was Jim's.

There were four hundred men in the column, all packed on cars, standing or sitting, or anyhow. And they sang

A rig' a de jig, and a-way we go
A-way we go, a-way we go,
A rig' a de jig and a-way we go
I. O. I. O. I. O.

And as the cars drew away out into the distance they could hear it, and Evelyn kept murmuring, "Oh, Jim, Jim, I didn't mean it." . . . and she thought her heart would break.

And she didn't know what she didn't mean except that she meant that she hadn't valued him properly, hadn't known how much she loved him, didn't mean to be so indifferent.

The train carried the column to Qu'Appelle and from there it struck across the prairies for the South Saskatchewan, trailing out in a strung-out line over the rolling hills and the soft green grass of early spring. They had the infantry out in front (the method used with the Moaris and in Ashanti), guns in file in the centre and the cavalry and the troops of horse behind them. That was because, with Moaris and Ashantis, if you lose the guns, its all over. The Queen's Intelligence came last. At night the column camped on its tracks round little fires of what brush and last year's grass would burn. The little army covered a mile of twinkling lights. The Queen's Intelligence sat round a brush fire of wood collected by Meadows, drinking whiskey poured out by Harris. Captain Despard explained how in mounted infantry you must keep clear of your horse in action, but if it's killed you can shoot from behind it.

Day after day the column moved. Night after night the lights twinkled.

All this came to Winnipeg by despatches sent back to the telegraph by despatch riders . . . COLUMN REACHES TOUCHWOOD HILLS . . . COLUMN NEARING SASKATCHEWAN . . . and with these came wires from the East . . . TORONTO FORCES

PASS LAKE SUPERIOR . . . MEN CARRIED IN SLEIGHS . . . REGI-
MENTS DUE WINNIPEG TOMORROW.

Then the troop trains reached Winnipeg, long trains made up of anything available. These were all sorts of soldiers in all sorts of uniforms, Tenth Royal Grenadiers from Toronto in a scarlet so bright that an Indian couldn't miss them at half a mile, and the Queen's Own Rifles in blue so dark that you could see them, against a light background, five miles away— and the Governor General's Body Guard, real cavalry, the only ones in Canada, all silver and blue. The town was just a roar of steam whistles and cheers of welcome.

But they had only half an hour in the town . . . went swinging along main Street with the Grenadiers singing

Litoria—Litoria—sweedle-e-wet—chu—hi—re—sa.

which was the great marching song of volunteers in the 80's.

And the Queen's Own Rifles singing the new song, or new at least to the West.

There is a tavern in the town . . .

But in just no time they were off . . . off west over the railway and then trailing over the prairies and foothills, the Grenadiers in a long red line, moving fast to catch up with Middleton's column . . . the others striking still further west to reach Poundmaker before he could join the half-breeds under Louis Riel and Gabriel Dumont.

Then the news came thick and fast . . . with crowds round the bulletin boards . . . and special extras. BATTLE AT FISH CREEK . . . COLUMN CHECKED BY HALFBREEDS—MANY KILLED AND WOUNDED—FIELD BATTERY CHECKS REBELS.

The halfbreeds and Indians under Louis Riel and Gabriel Dumont had waited for the column, strung out among the grass and shrubs of a coulee beside the Saskatchewan. They fired, hidden in the grass and the hollows, at men in uniforms of bright scarlet. The Field Battery, on the slope behind, threw shells with nothing to shoot at. Jim worked with a bandaged hand. He had to. There were two men dead under the gun. The Queen's Intelligence were in the thick of it . . . "Why doesn't Middleton rush them?" E.P. said. "Why doesn't the old fool rush them?" A lot of men said that. But Middleton was still sneering at his "raw soldiers."

Then came the night and enabled them to retire back over the brow of the coulee.

The Queen's Intelligence sat round their fire that night, jolted but full of fight. "That old fool," said E.P., "should have gone right on." In the rebel camp a couple of miles away some of them had the same idea. "Keep at 'em," said Gabriel Dumont, a veteran of the plains. "Don't let 'em sleep—treat 'em like buffalo—creep in on 'em—keep shooting at 'em—scare 'em." But Louis Riel had no stomach for it. He had never seen a big fight before . . . The dead and wounded round the camp turned him pale . . . He stood babbling over a crucifix . . . "No, no," he said, "enough blood, enough blood, *assez de sang*."

All that came into Winnipeg. Then the news of the attack by the other column on Poundmaker's Crees at Cut Knife. They were driven back. Then more soldiers came to Winnipeg, French regiments from Quebec, New Brunswickers, and more columns went across the plains. There followed the big fight of three whole days against the rifle pits at Batoche on the South Saskatchewan, and at last General Middleton did let the men go right at it, and charge the rifle pits and the log shelters; whether he let them or they let themselves, when that was done it was all over in an hour. Riel tried to get away. They caught him and brought him in, a shabby, disconsolate figure, the life all out of him, ready for the gallows. Gabriel Dumont got away and struck for the American border. Poundmaker and his Crees came in to surrender when they heard of Batoche. Middleton took the surrender seated on a camp chair, in the approved fashion used at Ashanti, or at Kabul. All of this moved so fast with such life and colour in it that it filled the Canadian press with headlines, and once or twice even got to New York and over to London. "AFFAIR ON THE SASKATCHEWAN" they called it.

All that was left presently was to round up Big Bear, and his lesser chiefs, the bands of Indians who had taken Battleford and Fort Pitt and made the massacre at Frog Lake. They were now somewhere up in the wooded country beyond the North Saskatchewan, making for the Athabasca wilderness, scattered bands of Indians that in the sequel it took all summer to find.

Then E.P. got another idea. The Queen's Intelligence must now make a *coup*. He would turn them into "flying columns" of "vedettes." He marked it all out for Despard on the map of the continent engraved on the back of his Arctic Railway Charter. "We cross here . . . we strike here . . . then we strike there" . . . the map was mostly fancy as he had drawn it for the engraver himself. But that made no difference . . . a Flying column must fly. "Who are we chasing?" asked Captain Despard. "Anyone we find," answered E.P.

They left that night—with no other authorization beyond

E.P. telling a sleepy camp adjutant that they were going out as "vedettes" to bring back intelligence of Big Bear, or of any other random Indians.

The adjutant didn't care where they went, or what they went as.

The Intelligence Corps went out over the plains and across the North Saskatchewan, making for the timber country. On the second day beyond the river, reached and "stalked" a settler's cabin. The settler being stalked said there were no Indians within a hundred miles, but didn't mind if he took a glass of whiskey. Two days later they stalked another settler and he took another. The night after that they reached the "timber," and sat under the trees round a fire, for it was cold though it was now June.

There they drank their drinks, poured by Meadows while Harris, the despatch rider, picketed the horses. The firelight playing on the group made it a wonderful picture; so wonderful that it was seen a quarter of a mile away by the Indians of Hole-in-the-sky and Thunder Man . . . These were two chiefs of Big Bear's outfit with a hundred braves with them, breaking north after the news of Batoche. The Intelligence sat thus drinking its whiskey and E.P. was saying at the second round, "Vigilance! vigilance! In dealing with Indians, one must never lapse for a moment. Stop! Wo! Plenty, thank you, Meadows." And they never saw the feathered heads and the painted faces, creeping nearer and nearer among the trees . . .

It was all over, with one wild war cry and one bound forward, except that Harris, the despatch rider got away—all over, and they were bound and tied, captives of Hole-in-the-sky and Thunder Man. Harris's escape made headlines in the Canadian papers. QUEEN'S INTELLIGENCE 'CORPS' CAPTURED BY BIG BEAR'S INDIANS. But it reached England as "CAVALRY COLUMN WIPED OUT."

Now that sounds like the beginning of horrors, of torture at the stake, of massacre. Not for a minute; not with such a mind as E.P.'s, dealing with such simple intelligences as those of Hole-in-the-sky and Thunder Man. They had hardly got him bound before they were untying him again. He effected it with his picture of the Queen, drawn out before he had his arms tied. These were Wood Crees who had never seen a photograph. They thought it a spirit, the spirit of the Great White Mother. E.P. said she had sent him to them to pardon them. Big Bear must be hanged (as a matter of fact he was not) but the Great Mother loved Hole-in-the-sky and Thunder Man and wanted them to live. He had the pardon in his pocket. Then he took out the Charter of the Arctic Railway, and all the Indians crowded round and grunted. He said that this pardon forgave all the band and he asked for an interpreter to read it off in Cree, and a Medicine Man took it and read it in Cree—just what E.P. said it was.

So the Indians let them all loose. That evening E.P. taught Hole-in-the-sky and Thunder Man to play poker with Despard's pack of cards. The next day he taught all the band to shout, *"Ho! ho! Victoria!"* and lift up their tomahawks high in the air. They learned it so well that when two days later the relief column of one hundred Northwest Mounted Police came tearing over the prairie to the woods and deployed into line and swung off saddle with the precision of trained cavalry and then began to stalk the wood, with rifles ready—all

the band came out from the trees with E.P. at the head . . .
"Ho! ho! Victoria!"

The rest, all the way to Middleton's column, just leaving,
and with it to Winnipeg, was sheer triumph. The headlines
said FLYING COLUMN CAPTURES CREES.

So they got back to Winnipeg and all the town was tumult
of welcome, with military bands playing and everyone a hero,
and civic receptions and reviewing of the troops. Then came
the leaving of the troop trains for the East, crowded and singing and triumphant—going home.

And then it was all over. How quickly glory passes! All
over and forgotten it seemed in a week. E.P. was back in his
shabby house, talking of cables expected from the new mines
of Johannesburg, his last bulwark against the creditors who
had all flocked back. Evelyn was typing and Jim selling
stamps again, with one hand, at the Parliament Building . . .
General Middleton had spoken highly of Jim after Fish
Creek, and a lot of people had noticed him and there might
be a good job for him presently; in fact, there was right now
a fine partnership he could have if he could put up $5,000.
But things were so dreary now that E.P. didn't even offer to
cable the British Treasury.

And Evelyn said, "I wish mother were back. Oh! I wish
mother were back."

And she was much nearer to being back than Evelyn had
any idea of. For in England everything had failed her. Each
night, after the latest lawyer's letter came to the vicarage, the
Vicar, her brother-in-law, would sit in his little study in the

vicarage adding up figures, and would say, "Dear me, dear me, how unfortunate."

Like so many estates, the more they wound it up the smaller it got. "I'm afraid I don't really understand business, Agness," said the Vicar. "We didn't learn it at Cambridge—but I'm just afraid, that really there's nothing there—or only just enough to pay your passage back." So her brother-in-law advanced Agnes enough out of what the lawyers advanced him out of what the estate advanced them. And Agness left for Canada. The Vicar drove her in a donkey cart over to the railway junction at Muddle-on-the-Edge, and he kissed her good-bye.

And from there she went third class to London, and from there third class to Liverpool and from there second class to Montreal, and from there by no class at all was on her way to Winnipeg—only a few hours away when Evelyn spoke.

. . . "Unless," E.P. had said, "I get a cable," and after they had gone out he had sunk into a chair, and sat there, the outspread newspaper on his lap, beaten at last—or else playing at being beaten at last.

Yet if he had known it there was a cable coming, but coming from so far away—from half round the world, that it was not there yet though it had started the morning of the day before in Gujahar, North India. If this were a moving picture we could follow the progress of the cable from Gujahar to Winnipeg in a set of variegated scenes. It was written and put on the wires in mixed English and Gujahari by a cinnamon-coloured telegraph clerk in a white suit with a black band on one arm to mean that the Maharajah of Gujahar was dead (the old Maharajah), and a sky-blue band on the other to mean that the new Maharajah was alive. The address was the hard part, for it ran Mrs. Dacres, The Vicarage, Little Bosing-on-the-Edge, Edgewater, via Exeter, England. The yellow clerk worked with the address, consulting a big Guja-hari dictionary. After the address the rest was Gujahari and went like lightning.

That took the cable as far as Calcutta where a brown Baboo telegraph clerk in white with a white puggaree ran it all into what he understood was English, correcting Vicarage to Vicquorage, and with that it went on to Aden in one jump. There a telegraph clerk in a white uniform with a pith hel-met, because he was also a subaltern of engineers, took the cable and when he wrote it out he said, "I say, I'll be damned! Do look at this, Charteris." And Charteris said, "I say . . . I *will* be damned." Six officers were damned. They all knew of course that the Maharajah of Gujahar was dead because in Aden there's nothing else to know except that sort of thing. But they all exclaimed when they saw the message, "All that money! Eh? What? But it's only fair—the old boy simply stole it."

Then the cable went on another jump to Suez. And there an Egyptian clerk in a white suit and scarlet tarbosh ran it off into French, English not being allowed on the Mediter-ranean cable in 1885, and sent it on to Marseilles in one long throw. He made no change except to write Vikkerij. At Marseilles, an envious French telegraph clerk in a suit that had been white last year took the cable off the wire and wrote it out, held it up to the other clerks and put his fingers on the figures in it and said, *"Quelle veine, hein? Parlez-moi de ces Anglais!"*

The French clerk corrected the Turkish spelling Vikkerij to "Viqueurage." That took it to London and there it only took two minutes to make it "Vicarage," and send it from London to Edgewater, and within two minutes more a postman was carrying it from Edgewater to the village shop that was the post office in Little Bosing-on-the-Edge. But as it was sealed he didn't know what was in it and just whistled away as he walked. But he looked at the cable three or four times a minute. When he took it in, the postmistress looked at it— from above and from below and sideways. They both did . . . and she said, "Why, it's a cable, dear me! From Googe —from Googe . . . Suppose I've got to open it." "That's regulations, Mrs. Treloar," said the postman. "You deliver a telegram, as you might say, intact; a cable, so the regulation is, you open, for you can't tell . . ."

But by this time Mrs. Treloar had read it with one long snort of astonishment.

Mrs. Dacres, The Vicarage, Little Bosing-on-the-Edge, Edgewater, via Exeter, England. British Government arbitration tea plantation claims against late Maharajah Gujahar awards you fifty thousand pounds sterling.

And with that the postman and postmistress started a race across the common to the Vicarage, knocking over sheep as they ran . . . through the gate they burst and through the door. The Vicar was just reading a morning prayer to his wife in the drawing-room, the day's lesson out of St. John, *"And they said, lo! where may we look for help?"* When they broke in both shouting, "Gujahar!" The Vicar read the cable, and his wife fell on the neck of the postman and sobbed.

The Vicar was prompt. He had the donkey cart out within an hour. Within two he was at the cable office in Exeter, and it was still that same morning in Winnipeg when the knock of the telegraph boy come to E.P.'s door.

"I've got a cable here," he said. "It's for your wife—is that all right?"

"A cable?" said E.P. in surprise, then he remembered and said, "Yes, that's all right. Another cable, eh?" Then he read it: *British Government arbitration tea plantations claims against late Maharajah Gujahar awards you fifty thousand pounds sterling.*

"Good Lord!" said E.P. "fifty thousand pounds!" Then, "Here boy!" and he began plunging his hands into his pockets . . . "Here, boy." But there was nothing. Then he said, "Come," slapped on his hat, grabbed the boy by the wrist and with the cable in the other hand dashed into the street.

He bumped into a clergyman. "Good-morning," the clergyman began sweetly. "Give this boy a dollar," said E.P. In sheer surprise the clergyman gave it. They bumped into a grocer watering window boxes in front of his store. "Give him a dollar," E.P. gasped. The boy got four dollars before E.P. let him loose at the door of the bank.

"I must see the manager," he said at the counter, "see him at once." The manager stepped from his office. "I'm sorry," he said with a frozen face, "we can't possibly advance another cent. Our head office . . ."

But E.P. had recovered all his old power. "I want to scratch off a cheque for a thousand dollars. They want me at once in Gujahar. The Maharajah has just cabled."

The manager collapsed into a wet rag. The money was paid across. Within half an hour all the saloons in Winnipeg had heard of the Maharajah of Gujahar. E.P. was lined up with a row of pals—Count Fosdari, Captain the Honorable Desmond Despard and all comers.

"The Maharajah's cable, of course, means we are leaving for Gujahar at once."

In the next saloon he said the Maharajah wanted him to raise a troop of cavalry, and in the next, "I expect I shall be asked to command the entire army of Gujahar."

In the middle of the afternoon a second cable, this time from the Bank of England and addressed again to his wife, said, *Placing fifty thousand sterling to your credit, Winnipeg.* After that E.P. said, "It's very likely, of course, that they'll want me to take over three of four of the Native States."

At which E.P., now in possession of boundless money, moved with his old energy. The first thing was to set his house in order.

So when Jim and Evelyn got to the house that evening the place was transformed. They could see it half way down the street as a blaze of light. There had been so many cleaning women working in the house that it smelt of gin. Delivery men were dumping in cut flowers and plants . . . Crockery and glasses were coming in crates. Half a liquor store had arrived. New carpets were going down. A "handy-man," half tight, was pounding them in with tacks.

Jim and Evelyn stood, open-eyed. "Why! Uncle Edward!" Jim began. "Why, father," said Evelyn. "I shall explain it all presently," said E.P. "It means that I shall probably leave for India as soon as I can arrange things with the Viscount. He may want to go by way of Japan. In any case, I shall only wait till I get your mother back. I'm sending Harris with a cable. She'll come at once, I'm sure."

Come? But she was there already—getting out of a cab in

the dusk, and wondering at the lights—and so happy to be there; so sad to bring nothing, but so glad to be back.

And in a moment she was in his arms . . .

"Agnes!" "Edward!"

There was dinner, real dinner, in the house that evening, with all the pomp that E.P. could throw into it, at such short notice . . . himself in evening dress, and Agnes in the things they wear in English vicarages. Jim was still in his Field Battery uniform. "You must excuse him not dressing, dear," E.P. said, "he's not supposed yet, of course, to be in mufti."

"Meadows," he said, "you can retire to your pantry when you have served the port. If I want Harris I shall ring."

But it turned out instead that in a few minutes Harris wanted him. Harris brought a cable, a real one, all paid for; and at last it was from London, from the office of Her Majesty's Secretary of War. It said:

Her Majesty desires me to express her appreciation of your gallantry for which you are to receive in due course the D.S.O. about to be instituted and the Honorary Rank of Colonel in the Imperial Forces.
                                                            Hartington.

Before dinner was over it had all been explained now about the Gujahar money. "It will make a very good start," said E.P., as he drank his port. "I shall cable at once to see about developing the Peace River and opening the Arctic Railway . . ."

His wife came round the table and put her arm around his neck . . . "Ned," she said, "suppose we don't cable any more, not to anybody. Let this be for us not a start but a finish—peace and happiness . . . Let it be a start for *them*."

"For them, of course, for them first, but for everybody,

too." E.P. rose to an attitude. "This shall make a new beginning for the West . . . all my dreams . . . all my visions shall come true . . . I see it coming . . . four million . . . this city half a million . . . the star of the Empire shall glitter in the West and shall never set."

XVI

MARIPOSA MOVES ON

Introduction

PEOPLE who still entertain a kindly remembrance of *Mariposa*, the scene of my *Sunshine Sketches of a Little Town* of many years ago, will pardon me if I append these further sketches of Mariposa in the shadow of war. They were written, as is obvious from the text, in connection with the Victory Loan of 1943.

But as *Mariposa* is not one town, but is at least several hundred in Canada and in the adjacent States, and as more Victory Loans may yet be needed for complete victory, it seems not inappropriate to find a place in this book for these Mariposa Sketches.

I

THE HAPPY WARRIOR

He came out to my house beside the lake—the most pleasant, cheery man I ever saw. I knew him just a little bit, but couldn't recall his name.

"Canvassing for the Loan," he said as he shook hands. "Pretty strenuous going!"

"Sit down," I said and showed him an easy chair on the verandah.

"A great spot you have here," he remarked. "That's a pretty little bay."

"Yes," I said, "they call it The Old Brewery Bay."

"Well, well, The Old Brewery Bay!" he repeated. "That's a beautiful name! Poetic, isn't it?"

That's what I judge my visitors by.

If they like the name, The Old Brewery Bay, they're all right. They can have anything on the place. Once a woman —I won't say a lady—exclaimed, "Can't you change it?" . . . She got hers.

As a matter of fact I have known that name, The Old Brewery Bay, to make people feel thirsty by correspondence as far away as Nevada.

"Pretty strenuous business," repeated my friend the canvasser, as he sat comfortably down. But he didn't look strenuous either.

"Will you have a cigar?" I said.

"I certainly will," he answered, and then as he lit it.

"Any fish in the bay?"

Well, of course, that started us. We got talking of bass being right in the bay and out on the shoals in July, but always moving on in August. I told him there were lots of young pickerel in June, close in along shore, but you could never make them bite; and he asked me if I'd ever tried a very small gilt and silver spinner for pickerel, and I asked him if he ever took Scotch whiskey.

That led to the question of trout fishing. If you don't see the connection it doesn't matter. But I agreed with him that nowadays if you go trout fishing on the streams you've got to carry soda. You can't any longer drink the water in the creeks.

That led to the discussion of the way the fish are disappearing in the older settled parts of Ontario and that you have to go north now. So we went north—taking another cigar and another Scotch with us—all the way up to Central Algoma.

Anyway, we spent a most pleasant hour or so. As my friend rose to go I suddenly remembered the Loan.

"You're canvassing for the Loan?" I said.

"Yes," he answered, "from a special list. You're on it."

"That's all right," I said. "I took up my subscription yesterday at the bank."

"So they told me," he said.

II

NATIONAL DEBT, NATIONAL BLESSING

I was a witness to a queer matter of psychology this morning. Psychology? No, I'm not trying to use a long word for a short. It's simple enough. It just means the way you use your mind. For instance, at poker, when you want the others to think you hold at least a straight, that's psychology. At golf, when you say to the caddy, "How many was that last hole?" and want him to say *seven* instead of *eleven*, that's psychology.

The case I mean occurred in the Mariposa barber shop that I've spoken of before—Jeff's place—a sort of centre of town talk and public information. I was sitting there in the barber shop waiting my turn—or—well, I won't say "waiting my turn" but waiting till I had, in fairness, to accept my turn. You see, here in Mariposa it's not like in the City. The barber shop—I always go to Jeff's—is a comfortable place to sit in with as good conversation and as much information as you get in any first class club. So each one likes to sit as long as he can till Jeff nominates him to a chair. When he says, "You're next," you have to take your place. You've read about the guillotine.

It was in the quiet hour of the morning with only Jeff himself shaving. But I got nominated to the chair almost right away because the morning papers had just come off the bus and most of the fellers preferred to sit and read for a while.

Well, Bill Landy was talking to George Summers and evidently talking Victory Loan.

Bill Landy has a mind as quick and bright as the flight of a humming-bird. He has to. He's in the mining stock business and in that you mustn't give the other man time to think. Of course Bill is closed just now, so he's in war work— a dollar a year man—the most he ever made, net. He's the chief canvasser for the Loan in Mariposa—not the Chairman of the Committee, though—Mariposa is too religious a place to make a mining broker a Chairman.

Anyway, Bill was talking to George Summers. George is different. He has a cement business, and you know the way it is with cement. It has to settle. George's mind is like that. You can't make any marks on it—he won't let you—till it gets set and firm. George laid the town sidewalks and he doesn't forget the place where the duck walked across the cement in front of the Public Library. No, sir.

I didn't hear how the talk, or argument, started because Jeff had put a hot towel over my face and stopped to listen and forgot me. But when he let me out of the chair Bill Landy was saying,

"At any rate, you remember the old phrase, a national debt is a national blessing."

"Why do you call it a phrase?" says George.

"Because it is."

"Is what?"

"Is a phrase," says Bill.

"Never mind the phrase business," interrupts one of the boys who was listening. "Where does the blessing come in? Isn't a debt a debt?"

"Why, this way," says Bill. "You take a national debt like ours, widely distributed—"

"What do you call distributed?" asks George.

"He means everybody holds some," says one of the fellers.

"Oh!"

"Well," Bill went on, "now let's say that individual A holds a hundred dollars—"

"Who's he?" asks George.

"Well, just A, or if you like, I'll call him B."

"No, no, call him A if you like. You mean some feller whose name begins with A, like Alec Anderson or Andy Ames."

"Yes, exactly, but I don't mean *them*."

"Oh, you don't!"

"He just means anybody," interrupts the Chorus.

"Yes," says Bill, "I just mean a whole string of individuals: A, and B, and C, all the way to Z."

"I doubt," says George Summers slowly, "If you'd find any feller here in Mariposa whose name begins with Z."

"No matter," says Bill, "the point is this. Each hundred dollars that the government borrows means, to the government, a hundred dollars of debt . . ."

"Yes."

"But for A, B, and C, it means a hundred dollars as an asset."

"Right down to Z," says George, "or is there a catch in it?"

"Why, don't you see, George," interrupts me and the fellers in the seats, "what's a debt to the Government that it owes me, looks to me like an asset, a hundred dollars to the good."

"Exactly," says Bill Landy. "Now add up all the total. If the country owes a billion dollars, is it any poorer? No, not if it owes it at home. It means there are a lot of people in the country who are, put together, a billion dollars to the good. Make it two billion, it's all the same."

"And where's the blessing?" asked George.

"Holds the country together," says one of the listeners. "Who's going to upset or shipwreck a government if he depends upon it for three or four thousand dollars invested in a loan?"

"Exactly," says Bill Landy.

"I begin to see," says George Summers.

"Next!" called Jeff.

"You're next, George," said the boys. "Shave Mr. Summers, Jeff, we'll wait." They knew it was just the moment.

I walked out and down the street with Bill Landy.

"That's a hard business, Bill," I said, "canvassing a feller like George Summers."

"Oh, that was not for George," Bill said. "He'll take up the Loan good and plenty when he gets set. That was for the other fellers."

"How do you mean?" I asked.

"Why, the way to make a feller see anything, is to let him see some other feller not see it; d'you see!"

"I see," I said.

III

THE SULTAN SPEAKS FROM THE GRAVE

Would you believe it that for the last Victory Loan this little town of Mariposa, raised $640,000. Think of it! For a town of only 12,000 people; in fact, the Federal census makes it only 9,000. But that's crooked; Ottawa's jealous of us.

Anyway, that's what we raised last time. Compare that with the old days when European kings tried to raise money and thought a hundred thousand pounds a huge sum. You could do a whole Crusade on it. Or compare it even with modern days when the Sultan of Turkey used to raise Turkish loans and couldn't raise a hundred thousand pounds without executing half his cabinet and sending a bow-string to his Grand Vizier to choke himself with if he didn't put the loan over. I refer, of course, to the Sultan that used to be. There is no Sultan over the Turks now. They got rid of them and got a real leader, Mustapha Kemal, who said, "Let's be up to date," and they shouted "Attaturk!" . . . So now the Turks are right in it and get all the money they need by telephoning to Mr. Churchill. But I was thinking of the Sultan that I used to read about in the newspapers when I was a boy, Abdul Aziz, the bad man of Europe, and his "Turkish Bonds" that were just a joke for waste paper. And just as I was thinking of him, all of a sudden I met him—Abdul Aziz—right here on the main street in Mariposa. The other people thought he was just an Armenian selling rugs, a little shrunken, yellow man with a rug over his arm, fresh and bright from Samarkand (Ontario).

But I knew who he was right away. "Buy a rug," he said . . . And when I looked in his face I saw it was the Sultan— a case of that descent of the soul from body to body that the Greeks used to call Metempsychosis. Once learn that word and learn how to spell it, and you'll see translated souls walking the street every day.

A little later he came out to my house. "Buy a rug!" he said as he came up on the verandah. I shook my head. "May I sit down?" he said. "I need to rest." I knew he did; so did Judas Iscariot; Abdul Aziz, I was certain, had to walk forever. "Buy a Victory Rug," he said and then he added, "Could you lend me an old pair of pants?"

Then I knew he was the Sultan of Turkey, so I spoke up. "Abdul," I said, "am I right in saying that you never raised in any one single sum from and among your whole fifty million people as much as this town of Mariposa did in the last Victory Loan—$640,000?"

"It is true," he answered. "Never once. There was one time when we nearly did it. We had a splendid committee. They worked up enthusiasm. They beheaded the local council of every Turkish village. They tortured all the tax gatherers. They put the thing over with—what is it you call it?—a hurrah! We raised half a million dollars. When we reached the total we had a grand banquet with music, executed all the committee, and divided up the loan."

Abdul paused, thinking of the great days before democracy. Then he went on. "I don't see how you do it," he said. "Have you sent a bow-string to the Mayor to tell him to choke himself?" "No," I said, "not yet."

"How many bank managers have you executed?"

"None," I said, "so far."

"What leading pashas (business men, you call them, do you not?) have you buried up to the neck?"

"None," I said. "They're in it up to the neck, but we didn't bury them."

Abdul sighed and was silent. So I thought I'd tell him something.

"Abdul," I said, "the secret of the thing is mutual confidence, trust in one another, the thing you never had in Turkey in your time—each man willing to lend because he knows he has behind the loan the good faith of all."

"I see it," said Abdul with enthusiasm. "I learn quickly. Lend me a dollar till Tuesday."

IV

HAVE YOU GOT EVEN ONE CENT?

Professor Scott Byron gave a lecture yesterday afternoon up here in Jeff's barber shop in Mariposa. The professor had come up on the noon train from the City, where he is a professor, and always when he comes up, he goes over to the barber shop and gives a lecture.

You see, it's a real treat for a professor to be able to give a lecture under proper circumstances such as he can get in a barber shop. With the students it's different. It hasn't the same life to it. They just sit there and write down their notes and don't half appreciate a good thing when they hear it. The students say that Professor Byron's talks always have too many statistics. But in the barber shop, they never can get enough. The students say that Professor Byron thinks he knows it all. In the barber shop they know he does.

The Professor comes up to Mariposa pretty often. He's getting now just that first touch of old age, like September frost in a garden, that mellows a man and makes him cling to the things he's grown used to. The Professor, you see, always comes up to Mariposa for his vacations and he generally manages to have a fortnight at Christmas; he can usually snatch a week for the trout fishing in May and likes the break of a fortnight in early June for the herring fishing. Beyond that, he has to content himself with odd week-ends. He's a busy man. He says so himself. In fact, he's getting touchy about it.

When the Professor is going to lecture in Jeff's place he comes in to get his hair trimmed. Trimmed, you understand, not cut. Jeff understands it exactly; he just trims it round so that there's as much as ever and the Professor can come back next day and have it trimmed again.

I wouldn't mention all this except that it happened yesterday's lecture came in just right for Victory Loan week. I don't know whether the professor meant it that way but at any rate his talk was all about interest on money and how it increases if you let it alone. As soon as he said "interest" all the fellers in the shop were sure that he was hitting at the Loan.

What he told us was certainly curious. Some of the "boys" doubted it but Jeff himself believed it fully. You learn to believe when you run a barber shop.

He told us a story and he said you could prove it by any history book—that when the Dutch came to settle in America in 1621 they took the lower half of Manhattan Island—where New York City is located now—and they had too much conscience to take it from the Indians for nothing, so they gave them fifty dollars for it.

Imagine getting the best part of the City of New York for fifty dollars.

But Professor Byron claimed that the Indians got the best of the bargain. If the Dutch, he said, had put the fifty dollars out at interest and let it stay there, it would have brought in, by this time, more than the city is worth. Of course, the professor admitted that interest rates were higher then than now; people got ten per cent easy enough for business loans (kings paid up to twenty or more), and even a hundred years later eight per cent was easy enough.

Here's the way the professor worked it: Money at ten per

cent doubles in 7¼ years. He gave the Dutchmen ten per cent till 1735. Then eight per cent till 1835; money at eight per cent doubles in 9 years; he gave them six per cent till 1895 (he said the United States government itself paid that much in the Civil War time); money at six per cent doubles itself in 12 years; he gave them five per cent till 1923; at that, money doubles in 14 years: and four per cent till 1943, with money doubling in 17½ years.

This meant that every dollar the Dutchmen invested was doubled 35 times. It starts off as $1, $2, $4, $8 . . . and looks pretty harmless. But watch it when it gets going. When you get the total of 35 doublings multiply it by fifty because the investment is fifty dollars. It works out at something more than one and a half trillion dollars—$1,500,000,-000,000. That sum is 240 times the assessed value of all the land and all the property in Manhattan. It would buy all the United States.

The professor offered to calculate it all out and he asked Jeff if he had a table of logarithms. Jeff said he'd always wanted one in the shop (they look nice) and that his wife had tried to grow them in pots, but they came to nothing.

He was just going to throw the professor on his back and trim his moustache when he saw that Professor Byron was still talking, so he tilted him up and clipped his neck and let him go on.

This time it was William the Conqueror. "You've all heard of William the Conqueror," he said. All of the fellers said yes, and old Archie Green said he remembered him personally very well and that he always used to walk in six miles from the old Conyers place (it's on the fourth) every Sunday to the Presbyterian Church in Mariposa. Very erect, Archie said.

The professor got his neck up higher and said he meant the William the Conqueror who conquered England. And some one said, "What would Mr. Churchill say to that?"—and the lecture nearly went off the track, as lectures are apt to, in a barber shop. That's where students are better.

But the professor managed to get the audience back and what he told them was that if William the Conqueror when he marched into London had invested there one cent—just one single cent, and left it there, it would be worth now—well, I forget what—as much as that.

Jeff said it was certainly a caution, and some one else said that he supposed that if a feller took a good slice of this Victory Loan and just left it to increase, he might presently buy up the whole of Mariposa.

But the professor didn't stay for the discussion. He knew of another place where he could talk and he went out.

When he was gone someone said, "I'll bet the prof. buys in on the Loan, eh?"

There was a bank teller sitting there, a kind of smart feller and he said, "He has already. He put a cent in today."

V

THE RIGHTEOUS INDIGNATION OF
ANGUS McCORDELL

There is, of course, a radio in Jeff's barber shop in Mariposa. But Jeff never feels very sure about turning it on. People are peculiar. It's all right if it's baseball or anything like that, but Jeff says customers are touchy. Why he's known some people object even to the Farm and Produce Prices—get right up out of the chair—think of that!

Of course the war is all right, that is, when it's really war news, but Jeff says customers are apt to get a little restless if it's just war talk. He says a lot of it sounds too much like religion. He admits that no doubt it's not meant that way, but customers resent it all the same.

So Jeff finds that the best plan is just to keep the radio going quietly so that in a way you hear it and yet it doesn't interrupt anybody. Jeff himself is fully satisfied with the result because no doubt being right there beside the chair he can keep one ear each way. You have to, anyway, in running a barber shop.

But for people sitting round the shop it's different. It sounds like alternate talk, first this, then that, especially as the customers pay no attention to what is very often earnest pleading and butt right in on it. Perhaps the radio speakers have got into a set, stereotyped way that fails to carry conviction. That may be it. If so, the customers are not so wrong.

The talks run something like this: . . . "Surely we realize that in this great world struggle for freedom we ought to feel that no effort is too great."

. . . "With a good push Toronto could move up into second place. That must be a dandy pitcher, that new feller they have . . ."

"That's so."

. . . "Is it not then our duty towards all that we cherish . . ."

"How are the roads out past Medora?" . . . "I didn't come that way. I went round by the third, but they are not apt to be any too good at this time of year. Of course, with plenty of gravel . . ."

. . . "The Hun can be crushed, will be crushed. We must be strong and spare not till the whole foul brood of Naziism has been extirpated and then . . ."

. . . "Potatoes will be up to three dollars for dead sure . . ."

That's the way it generally went and we got used to it. But last Monday afternoon it was different. There were quite a few people in the barber shop and naturally they were talking about the Loan and one fellow—I won't name him, but it was Pete McGaw—said he didn't see much profit in taking three per cent when a fellow could easy get six on a town mortgage. And he said he wasn't taking any of the Loan. And quite a few fellers—it wouldn't be fair to give their names; Joe Ekers was one—spoke up and said they'd no idea of taking any.

You see it just happened that way. Fellers are like that. Now another day it might be just the other way.

Well, just then there was a man who began to talk over the radio who *could* talk. Yes, sir. And he was talking of righteous indignation and when he spoke of it he sent a tingle through your blood and heroism to your heart. I don't know who he was. If you heard him you'll remember it was a voice with a strong Scottish accent and there was truth and power in every word.

"Don't be afraid to be angry, to be crazy angry, to be filled with righteous indignation. Nothing else has ever won a war. Nothing ever will, nothing but the flaming righteousness of the spirit that counts death as nothing."

The shop grew still and even Jeff stopped the clippers from clipping.

The voice went on:

"All history shows it, the history of your country here and of mine at home. What but the power of the spirit ever animated the men of Scotland to stand firm to death at Culloden and wring victory from Waterloo. I tell you, strike these people down! Kill and spare not! Death is their portion!"

Sitting against the wall of the barber shop was a big crooked Highland man, too tall, as they all are, to sit properly anywhere, and as he listened to the radio I could see his fingers buckle and clench and the fire flash in his blue eyes. This was Angus McCordell, the "crazy Highlander." We all knew him. Below the tam-o'-shanter that he wore there was a deep mark furrowed along the side of his head. That was from the battle of the Somme; and the two bent fingers of his left hand were from after he went back again; and the half limp in his leg from the third time. He had blue eyes and a clear face and a stubble beard, half red, half grey. He was twenty years old at the Somme. So that will give you his age.

That was Angus McCordell and he lived by himself out on

the fifth concession and some people said he was crazy and some said half crazy.

He was a wild man anyway. When he got angry nothing stopped him. He reached for his double-barrelled gun and started after somebody. There were car thieves around Mariposa one summer, terrorizing the farms outside the town. Angus went after a gang of five. One he shot full of buckshot, and one dead. The rest got away in their car. There've been no car thieves round since.

Show Angus any wrong or cruelty and he'd flame up at once, and go for his gun and get after it. That was all right and no doubt made for righteousness. But at other times Angus would take fire at some purely imaginary idea in his crazy Highland head and come raging into town with his gun, looking for trouble. Then the Chief of Police, who was Scottish himself, would chase after Angus and drive him out home in his car. So that was why people said that Angus McCordell was crazy.

The radio appeal ended with a call to give . . . give . . . give—that those who held back were unworthy to be citizens . . .

As it ended, Angus jumped up from his seat, shaking his clenched hand.

"Yon's right," he said. "The man who won't give to this Loan is unfit to walk the street. He's a damned German. He should be shot in his tracks."

And he stormed out of the shop.

"Who's that?" said an alarmed city customer, crawling out from under a Russian shampoo.

They all told him in a babble. "He's gone for his gun," they said. "He'll be back in an hour, raging up and down

Main Street, looking for a man who hasn't subscribed to the Loan."

Peter McGaw was out first. They said he was over in the bank in two minutes, signing up for five hundred dollars. Joe Ekers was right after him. He was saying to the tellers that it would be a good thing if every feller who subscribed to the Loan could wear a white band, or something, on his arm so that people would know him on the street.

As the news about Angus went round town you could see men streaking from all directions to the banks. There were so many they had to wait in line.

Angus came sure enough—with his double-barrelled shot-gun—raging up and down the Main Street. The Chief of Police refused to stop him. "He's done nothing," he said. "He's made no threat against any assignable person. He's said he'll kill any Hitlerite in Mariposa. He's entitled to. He says he'll put a charge of buckshot in any Nazi who refuses to subscribe to the Victory Loan. He's within his rights."

The chief, as I said, was from the Highlands himself.

There was great relief that evening when Angus went off home. But it ended abruptly the next morning when he came back. In fact, things were worse. On the first day, to most people, it was no matter of personal alarm; indeed it was more or less a good joke on the slackers. But this next morning Angus was parading up and down the street in a sort of military fashion. He'd got a new idea. He was after the whole town now. He said that Mariposa had to raise its Quota—that sum that it was pledged to raise. Raise that, he said, or he'd shoot up the whole street.

But the trouble is, the Quota was put too high; everybody

knew that. You know Mariposa. It was just vain glory and civic pride. They never expected to raise it.

Angus is on the street right now. The Chief of Police won't interfere. He says let them raise the Quota.

Most of them think they will. In fact, they're all at one another to do it. Angus will see that they do.

Nothing like righteous indignation, is there?

VI

THE CHAIRMAN'S WALKING STICK

It was pretty well understood by the middle of the Victory Loan Campaign in Mariposa that on the final evening they would present the Chairman of the Committee with a stick. This was partly on the Chairman's own account. Jim Heavyside—that's the older one; don't confuse him with young Jim —is one of the biggest business men in Mariposa, head of the largest of the companies, and just retired from active work a month ago after a long life of service to the town. And now he's thrown himself into this campaign with all his old time energy. In any case he's a good feller; I mean he's all right.

It has always been the thing in Mariposa to give a man a walking stick in recognition of any public service. They gave a stick to the designer of the historic monument in the Park, and a stick for the Municipal Abattoir, and a stick for the new wing of the Asylum that increased its capacity three to one and definitely put Mariposa on the map as a home for the feeble-minded.

Generally when they're going to give a stick the idea gets started and goes round town, confidentially, of course, so that the man himself won't know it. In this case, as a matter of fact, the idea originated in Jeff's barber shop and it was Jeff himself who first started it. He stopped his scissors one afternoon and rested his elbow on the customer's neck and said, "What about a stick for Jim Heavyside?"

The idea caught right on. And Jeff—you know how a

modest man gets encouraged and goes on—said that to his mind, one of these Malacca canes with a band on it would be just right. It appears that they sell canes like that clear up to a hundred dollars, and past it, though you wouldn't think it.

Well, that was all settled and the next thing was to raise the money. Bill Landy—he's the mining broker I spoke of—generally does that because he understands finance. He just gets from each feller what he feels like giving, and keeps it confidential. He gives out nothing except the total. A lot of mining business is done that way. They just tell you what you get.

So that was all settled, and Bill got busy and a couple of days later he was telling a group of us in the shop that he had all the money for the cane in sight, when who should walk in but Jim Heavyside himself. He was leaning on a Malacca cane. You could have knocked any of us down with a club.

One of the fellers, in a chair, who could only half see, called out, "What's the matter, Jim, gone lame?"

"No," said Jim Heavyside with a laugh, "the boys at the factory gave me a farewell supper last night and this stick as a presentation. That's the third stick," he added, "that I've got in less than a month. Take a look at it; isn't it a dandy?"

They passed it round but of course the heart was out of the idea now. They had to think of something else.

Well, the next day, Jeff said to some of the customers in the shop, "Professor Byron was up here from the City yesterday and he says why not give Mr. Heavyside one of these sets of books—what is it—an encyclopaedia?"

"An encyclopaedia," said one of the fellers. "Why, Jim Heavyside could never read that. He's no scholar."

"You don't have to *read* an encyclopaedia," says another. "It is for the front room. And when you buy them now they sell you a glass case right with them so that you don't have to open it even for dusting. Bert Trawley has one—has had it for ten years—and it's in dandy shape—good as new—they never open it."

"Grandfather had one," said another customer, "given to him like this when he retired, but he *read* his; yes, sir, sat down to read it clear through and get the good out of it. But he was too old when he started. He died in the letter A. But Jim Heavyside is only sixty-five. He can tackle it."

So it was settled that the presentation gift would be an encyclopaedia. But just to avoid all error this time they got Bill Landy to go up to the Heavysides' house to spy round and see if they had one.

Lucky they did. They had one sure enough, and a real beauty, an antique, in fine old leather, at least seventy years old. Goodness knows what it would fetch today. So that was a lucky escape from another bad break.

Then came a suggestion that carried every one with it. It's a wonder that so often the right thing never occurs to any one at first. This idea like so many others, came from Peter Cogland, the new lawyer in Mariposa. He's always full of ideas and popular. Of course, he's new to Mariposa—only been here six years—but the feeling is that after he's been in the town a while and gets settled, he'll play quite a part.

Anyway, it was Peter who said, "Why not give Jim Heavyside a case of Scotch Whiskey?" Well, the idea just caught like wild fire.

Someone said, "But Jim doesn't drink," and Peter said, "That doesn't matter. You see, he has to entertain a lot, and now all the more because of this campaign and being retired. He'll have fellers in his house all the time. This whiskey will come in just right. But listen—a case is only two dozen isn't it—we might make it two cases—one for Jim and one for Mrs. Heavyside." "That's right," said one of the boys, "the only question would be whether Scotch whiskey is as acceptable as gin—a case of real old dry gin—"

"Or if you come to that," interrupted George Summers, "what about a case of rye?"

But he was ruled out. Everybody knew that George only drank rye.

The only question was whether such a presentation was legal. Would the law of the province allow it or not! So Jeff said, "I tell you boys, why don't you telegraph down to the city and ask if it's legal to give the Chairman of a Loan Committee a case of whiskey? I can't express it right," said Jeff, "but no doubt Mr. Cogland could."

So Peter Cogland got a pencil and a pad and they started framing a telegram to the Attorney General's Office. It was certainly hard to phrase.

"A group of citizens of Mariposa desire to know . . ."

That didn't sound right.

"On behalf of the undersigned group . . ."

And that sounded wrong.

"Would you consider a case of Scotch whiskey . . ."

No, that sounded backwards.

Then someone suggested, why shouldn't they write it just the way Jeff said it:

"Is it legal to give the Chairman of our Loan Committee a case of whiskey?"

So that was what they sent.

Telegrams are like that.

The answer came right back while most of them were still sitting round discussing it.

"Presentation entirely legal. Writing you to that effect."

So that was great. They started right away picking brands of a Liquor List, each one what he liked best.

Naturally there were quite a number of fellers in the shop next day when the noon mail came in. The letter was addressed to Jeff and it read:

"Your proposed presentation of one or more cases to the Chairman of your Victory Loan Committee is entirely within the law. The only limitation upon it is that the cases must not be bought for this purpose but must be filled with bottles taken from the private stock of individual subscribers."

Well, say! . . . Talk about a Victory Campaign—talk about sacrifice and winning the war—but when it comes to . . . well, I mean when you ask a man to—well, who would want to . . . oh, no, reason is reason.

So that was the end of that. I will admit that for the moment all the fellers looked pretty downhearted, almost felt mean. They knew that they were right in not asking one another to give up private whiskey but somehow they didn't feel so good.

Luckily there came to Peter Cogland on the spur of the moment one of those bright ideas that will some day send him to Ottawa—or half way to it. Anyway—as far, say, as Kingston.

"I've got it," he said. "We'll give Jim Heavyside a hundred-dollar Victory Bond."

Wasn't it simple? And timely? And obvious? And yet no one had thought of it. It's always like that. Give the Chairman one of his own Bonds! Why, of course!

So the meeting—it was a sort of meeting—broke up with enthusiasm and went to dinner.

I lingered behind a moment.

"That's fine, isn't it?" I said. "That was the real solution."

Jeff shook his head.

"I don't know that I hold with it," he said. "You give a man one of his own Bonds and it seems like giving milk to a milkman—or it's like giving me a free shave and a shampoo." And he added gloomily, "Jim will be disappointed about the stick."

"About the stick?" I said.

"Yes, he is expecting it. He'd heard something about it. He's got the notion of sticks. You see, Jim Heavyside is not vain but he's pretty proud of having three sticks given to him, and he was hoping to make it four. That's why he came down here with the Malacca cane . . . In fact, it was my idea. I said to him, "Mr. Heavyside, if you'll come down to the shop and bring one of your sticks that'll put the boys on their mettle to give another."

Luckily it hasn't been too late. Everything is arranged and the Chairman will get his stick. We have it all ready, and a real dandy. Some of the fellers think it must be worth a hundred and fifty dollars, some more. No one knows how much Bill Landy collected or what he paid for it. "Better taste," Bill said, "to keep it confidential."

VII

GOING! GOING! GONE!

Next to me in Jeff's barber shop in Mariposa there sat this morning a country feller, at a guess, from thirty-five to sixty-five years old.

"Were you **out** at the sale at Crittenden's yesterday?" he asked.

"No," I said, "where's Crittenden's?"

"Crittenden's!" he answered in amazement. "Why, right next the Ames place."

"Where's that?" I asked.

"The Ames place? Just beyond Lem Crowder's."

I let it go at that.

"No," I said, "I wasn't there."

"Well, sir," said the country feller, "you'd oughter been. It was a caution. I seen a sulky go for thirty dollars."

I didn't know whether that meant a lot or a little. But the audience in the barber shop did. "Gosh!" they said.

"Yes, sir, a sulky ten years old and with a broken trip, for ten dollars more than it cost ten years ago."

"There was an old lumber wagon there," said a man from across the room, "fetched a hundred and fifty dollars."

"Gosh!" said the room.

"I suppose," said the country feller to me, "you wouldn't be much interested in farm sales?"

No, not altogether. Yet, as he said it, I was carried back sixty-five years in recollection and was standing in the April

229

sunshine in the slush and snow of a barnyard—a farm auction sale—while the purchasers—who didn't purchase (they had no money)—walked up and down among the lean cattle and the broken machinery for sale. The farmer of the farm was treating them to whiskey and laughing it off as best he could. He was "sold up" and was going to move, they said, to "this Manitobah."

Inside the farmhouse the woman—the lady of the farm— was cutting sandwiches for the purchasers who couldn't buy but could still eat. The children were helping her. I was one. I could hear the voice of the auctioneer—hear it still across sixty-five years of memory—calling:

"Now, gentlemen, this fine double-seated cutter, as good as new—what do I hear?—make me a bid, gentlemen! Come, give me a start! Four dollars? Thank you, four dollars! Going at four dollars. Going! Going! Gone, at four dollars!"

Those were the hard times of the seventies, with no war to brighten the economic outlook, when the government had to borrow a million dollars, but couldn't find it in Canada.

But one need not look back across sixty-five years of retrospect for the remembrance of auction farm sales, the tragedy of the Canadian countryside. Five years is enough. Just five years! To those stricken, hungry days when our ten million people had no one to kill and no one to feed but themselves. Right here in Mariposa, every month of May brought with the Spring birds the little leaflets, the "dodgers" that fluttered, pinned up to the telephone and light poles and pasted up in the window of the Mariposa *Newspacket:*

Auction Farm Sale
Lot this: Concession that
To be sold regardless of reserve price

And then follows the list. Stand here a moment and look upon it, and reflect upon the tragedy of our economic life that knows no stimulus but death.

Item 1.—Two-year-old grey mare—

Do you get that? That's Fancy, the family driving horse. They've had her for years and years on the farm. They must have had her for eight years. There's a boy now in Tunis remembers driving her. They loved her. That's why they put her down at two years. It's not a lie. She was still two years to them.

These two "excellent milch cows," part Jersey (never mind the other part) and these "mixed poultry"—all that in the life of a family—Going! Going! Gone!

Or look at the last item:

Household furniture, books—

Do you realize that those are the books that grandfather's father brought out from the old country, a hundred years ago? Look—Walter Scott's *Lady of the Lake;* half of part of Macaulay's *England*—nothing you read now of course . . .

And with that I came back to myself still in Jeff's barber shop and they were talking of the sale at old Tom Crittenden's place. They were saying that he "cleaned up" (their very phrase, taken from a fanning mill) fifteen hundred dollars. What else could he do but sell up, with both the boys, it appeared, overseas, and Sally. Tom himself is spry enough and not a day over seventy-five, but he and the old lady can't run the place alone.

And just as they were saying that in burst old Tom himself. When I say "burst"—that is, he appeared outside the glass door, leant his stick outside the door frame, pulled the door open a little, then got his shoulder to it, took up his stick again and burst in.

So there he was, hearty and hale, and evidently so tickled with himself that he could hardly hold it in. He didn't look the least bit like the people who used to be sold up in the seventies.

There was a chorus of "How are you, Mr. Crittenden?" . . . "How are you, Tom?"

The old man nodded around. "Just come over, Jeff," he said, "to get cleaned up." Then, unable to hold it any longer, he added, "I've just put fifteen hundred dollars across the street in this Victory Loan; yes, sir, fifteen hundred dollars."

That explained, you see, the need of a shave. Farmers, of course, are people who shave regularly; never miss a Saturday except in harvest. But when a farmer "hits town" one of the things to do is to get a shave—a real one—with a Roman massage, and a shampoo under machine brushes—facial massage, lilac powder and flapping towels—the whole thing.

"You're next," said Jeff, giving him "priority" over all candidates; "sit right down." And with that, Crittenden was draped and wrapped and pinned and whirling brushes played round his bent head. When anyone spoke to Tom, the barber stopped, Tom answered, and then Jeff went at him with the brushes again.

"You've sold your place, Mr. Crittenden?" said a customer.

"No, indeed, I didn't sell the old place; just sold off the implements and the stock."

"Couldn't work it, eh?"

"Not now, with just the missus and me, and the boys gone, and Sally."

"Where are the boys now, Mr. Crittenden?"

"Both overseas. Jim's in Iceland with General Montgomery and Dick's right there in London with General MacArthur. Oh, I follow it," added old Tom.

"Too bad, to lose all your implements," said a sympathizer.

"Oh, I ain't lost 'em. They don't take 'em away. They're right there to work the place with."

"But you lose the use of them?"

"No, sirree, I don't lose the use of them. I can use them as much as I like any time."

"So you've just lost the livestock?" put in another customer.

"No, not entirely. The folks don't want to take them away and so the missus and I still have them on condition we milk the cows and use the milk and eggs."

There was a man in the shop waiting for a shave, a traveller (you know what that is) up from the City.

"Say, mister," he said, "I don't quite understand this. You've sold out and you've got fifteen hundred dollars and yet you still have your place and everything else you ever had. How do you explain that?"

"I don't try to," chuckled the old man. "I leave that for Mr. Ilsley—all I know is that I got fifteen hundred in this Victory Loan—that's five hundred each for the boys and five hundred for Sally."

As the dialogue had progressed Jeff had gradually transformed old Mr. Crittenden—shampoo'd, massaged, shaved, creamed, powdered and, at the end, splashed with lilac till he smelt like the 24th of May itself—he was disengaged out of the chair, fit for the bees to settle on him.

"I don't have to explain it," repeated old Tom. "I leave that to these here economists."

I felt that was for me.

"You're right," I said, "as to the mystery of the economics of it—this mystery of the poverty of peace and the prosperity of war. It's an economic paradox . . ."

I saw Jeff look at me apprehensively at the word "economics." He knew by instinct that economics won't go in a barber shop. What's more, there'd been some talk there one day about cutting out unnecessary industries and some one had claimed that shaving was non-essential. Jeff himself claimed it a war service—look at all the great generals—you've seen these pictures of MacNaughton?

So, as I say, he looked apprehensive when I began to speak.

"What Mr. Ilsley intends to do," I continued, "is to make the most of every productive industry—like this farm of Mr. Crittenden's—and to keep the consumer away from everything not absolutely essential."

Jeff looked across again.

"You're next," he said.

VIII

A NEW HEAVEN AND A NEW EARTH

Well, the thing is done. The big Loan's been raised. Mariposa passed its quota of a million dollars at 9:30 A.M. this very morning. All the bells rang and the factory whistles blew, and all the people have been out on the street laughing and talking and congratulating one another. I haven't seen anybody work all day, except Jeff, the Mariposa barber and his four assistants. It's been a real day for shaving. There's war service for you. You see, there were quite a lot of fellers who took a pledge that they wouldn't shave till the million dollars was raised. Jeff's clearing them up first. Then there are all the fellers going to the big lunch at noon, and the big later evening dinner at six o'clock. Talk of essential industries, eh.

But, do you know, perhaps it's just as well that the Victory Loan Campaign is closing. It was beginning to have a queer effect on the town, disrupting its social life. You know, in a place like Mariposa you can't get along without certain fixed animosities, fixed oppositions—people who differ from other people, and even people who don't speak to other people because they differ from them.

Well, between ourselves, all that was beginning to break down. Quite frankly, people are not accustomed to such good will all round, and this Loan Campaign has been threatening to undermine our fixed way of living. I admit it's the price we pay for Victory in War. But all the same it's differ-

235

ent. When I see a man like old Major Henge shaking hands, right on the street, with a man like old Edward Flint, and asking him what's the news of his son at the front—and telling about his own boy, a prisoner of war in Germany—and forgetting that he is still holding old Flint's hand while he's talking—well, I ask myself what things are coming to.

I wouldn't believe it except that I saw it. I was there. I was walking down Main Street with Major Henge and I saw old Flint coming and wondered how we could dodge him. Look at it this way: Major Henge is a life-long conservative, a member of the Church of England—Edward Flint is a Liberal or worse, and never goes inside a church. It seems queer, doesn't it, that they would stand and talk right where everybody could see them?

But even that wasn't the half of it. You'd see Continuing Presbyterians, the strict ones who never used to drink anything but whiskey, sitting at a soda-water fountain beside a Baptist; or Roman Catholics attending meetings in the Protestant High School. You felt somehow as if society was breaking away from its moorings, as if we never would get back again to where we used to be. And if you said that to any of the people they said, "Why should we?"

They told me—I wasn't there—that the Church of England clergyman in his sermon last Sunday made a reference to "our Russian brothers." That's going pretty far, isn't it?"

Along with that there has been a lot of pretty wild talk as to what they want to do in Mariposa after the war. It seems that the Loan—the realization that they could raise a million dollars in a little town like ours—has gone to their heads. They say that if we could spend it for war, why not raise another Loan for peace? Why not spend money on better houses, better schools, do something for the children on a big scale—knock down the old Central School, not fit to teach a decent child in. If you said it was only the poorer children who went there, they answered, why shouldn't the poor children have as good a chance as the rich ones?

As old Oliver Croke, the grouchy lawyer (the town grouch) says, we might just about as well be in Russia.

And with that there went all sorts of what they called town planning. For instance, everybody has suddenly decided that Main Street is too cramped and narrow; they want to knock down one side of it and throw it into the lake. A meeting of all the business men on the north side voted for demolishing their side of the street—*their* side, mind you—isn't that magnanimous? the south side business men will probably vote to sacrafice their side—just taking what they get from the Government to rebuild. It's the new spirit, or rather the old, that St. Paul speaks of, each man seeking the other's wealth.

Everybody is so full of hope, too, about it all—hope and social betterment. They all agree that we must make a great effort to uplift the poor, only just now we can't find any poor.

The thing came to a head this afternoon at a meeting that we tried to have after the Loan Quota was declared. It was meant to be the annual meeting of the Conservative Party. The idea was to seize the moment of enthusiasm over the Loan and use it to enthuse the Conservative Party. And Angus Gorse says—he's an old friend of mine who is the local organizer of the party—you've got to catch the Conservatives while they are awake.

Well, the meeting was the flattest failure from the beginning. Major Henge who spoke at the start, began saying, "We must admit that the Liberal Party has done great service to this Dominion—" and what did the audience do but start to clap and stamp their feet. Well, you can't run a Conservative Party that way. As Angus said to me, the moment you get that sort of dry rot in the Party it's all over. There's no room for that good will stuff if you're out to win.

Things reached a climax when a speaker referred to Mr. Mackenzie King, the Prime Minister, as a "Great Canadian Patriot." That was pretty strong. Angus Gorse felt it necessary to appeal to the Chair; he said that he was sorry to criticize but he must ask whether such an expression was in order. The Chairman ruled that it was quite in order "provided the speaker meant it by way of a joke. As no doubt he did." The speaker said he meant it in real earnest. The Chairman said he must ask him to withdraw the expression; he would put it to them this way, he said: What would Mr. Mackenzie King himself think if he heard that his name had been used in this way in a Conservative meeting? After Mr. King's long years of devoted service—or rather, let us say, his long years of trying to delude the people of this country—it would be painful to him, as a man, even a low one, to hear that a Conservative Meeting had called him a Patriot. So the speaker said that he would withdraw the words but he gave fair warning that he was going to say them, to *shout* them, outside after the meeting. The Chairman said that that was all right and he was heartily in accord with him. Then someone called out, "Three cheers for—" and others called, "Order, Order," and there was quite a little confusion.

Then came the final surprise, the climax.

Our proposed candidate, Colonel Trelawney, stood up to speak. And when he spoke they were all still.

He spoke very quietly, never raised his voice. But they all listened. You see, he lost his son, his only child, in the first year of the War, and so it was thought that the people might show their appreciation of his son's sacrifice, by sending

Colonel Trelawney to Parliament. The strange thing was that no one would have thought of that before the war, because Colonel Trelawney was always so cold and distant and hardly seemed to know people on the street. Now, since he lost his son, he seems so quiet. They feel as if they knew him but they still can't speak to him.

Colonel Trelawney said that he would ask them to withdraw his name. He felt that the sitting (Liberal) member, elected for two Parliaments already, should be kept in. What we should do he said, was to elect the best man, whether he was a Conservative or a Liberal. There was no room now, he said, for such divisions.

After that there was nothing more to be said. The meeting adjourned.

I walked across from the meeting to Jeff's barber shop with Angus Gorse. Angus was greatly disturbed. He said that the weak spot in that argument was that if you tried to pick the best man, as likely as not you'd get a Liberal. Look, he said, at some of the skunks we've succeeded in electing in Mariposa in past years. Well, could you do that without party organization and party feeling? No, a skunk would be nowhere, never get in anywhere. Well, there you were.

Inside Jeff's place there was quite a crowd and excitement because, as I said, they were crowding in to get shaved for the big dinner—dinner at six o'clock, mind you. After that there was to be a general meeting in the Town Hall, and a big speaker up from the City. "That man," said Jeff, "when he gets well started is good for two hours, any time. You don't want to miss that."

I did. But I didn't say so.

The streets were full of people, all afternoon and till sundown, everybody talking and friendly, and all so easy with one another. It seems so different from what it used to be. But for the price paid for it, it would seem a wonderful world.

I was in Jeff's shop again just after sundown before starting to walk home. Through the window you could see, sideways, a little down the street, a knot of people gathering, and hear the beating of a drum, and voices singing, and then a speaker talking to the crowd.

As the man spoke, an echo, or an eddy, somehow caught up his voice and it came for a moment clear and distinct through the partly open window—"a new heaven and a new earth."

"What's that, Jeff?" asked a customer in the chair, "a Victory meeting?" "No," said Jeff, "it's nothing. It's just a religious revival."

"Oh," said the customer, "nothing real."

A new heaven and a new earth—the words seemed to echo still as I walked away from the town and beside the lake towords my home. The evening was closing in around me—as it is every evening at my age—and from the lighted town behind me, and in the evening breeze gathering off the lake, the sound still came—"a new heaven and a new earth."

FINIS